RADIO–ELECTRONICS
MADE SIMPLE

by

MARTIN SCHWARTZ

Formerly Instructor at American Radio Institute

Published by
AMECO PUBLISHING CORP.
275 Hillside Avenue
Williston Park, New York 11596

RADIO ELECTRONICS MADE SIMPLE

PRINTED 1975
All material in this book up to date.

Copyright, 1969
by the
AMECO PUBLISHING CORP.

Library of Congress Catalog No. 71-77332

Printed in the United States of America

PREFACE

The field of Radio and Electronics has been experiencing a most rapid rate of advancement. The future for this dynamic industry is sufficiently clear to attract the very best people into it. Nevertheless, there is still a tremendous shortage of personnel to occupy the many excellent positions that are presently vacant.

This book has been written in order to provide the many people who are interested in radio and electronics, either as a hobby or as a career, with a basic and fundamental background. No previous experience or specific education is required as this book is written in a simple and easy to understand manner. Using but a minimum of mathematics, it sets forth the basic concepts in a clear, non-technical manner. By means of every-day language, it explains the more difficult principles and scientific laws associated with this field.

The first three chapters of this book deal with basic electricity, magnetism and alternating current theory. Chapters 4 and 6 cover the principles of the vacuum tube. The uses of vacuum tubes in power supplies and audio amplifiers are taken up in Chapters 5 and 8, respectively. The remainder of the book explains the theory of transmitters and receivers, as well as the antenna system.

Since the last decade has seen a tremendous upsurge in the use of solid-state devices, a complete description of solid-state diodes and various types of transistors have been included. These are presented where applicable throughout the text and also as a separate chapter.

This is an ideal book for the beginner, the experimenter, the hobbyist, the hi-fi enthusiast and the serviceman. It is for anyone who wants to gain, with the least difficulty, a complete understanding of the fundamentals of radio and electronics. This book also serves as a stepping stone for further study in the more specialized areas of the electronics field.

New York, N. Y.   Martin Schwartz

TABLE OF CONTENTS

CHAPTER 1

DIRECT CURRENT

MATTER

Matter is a general term that is used to describe all the material things about us. Matter includes all man-made structures, liquids, metals, gases, etc. -- in other words, everything that has weight and occupies space.

All matter, regardless of size, quality or quantity, can be broken down into over one hundred different elements. Some of the more common elements are iron, copper, aluminum and oxygen. Elements may exist alone or they may exist in combination with other elements. For instance, copper wire consists only of the element copper; on the other hand, water is a combination of two elements, oxygen and hydrogen.

Each element can be broken down further into two different types of tiny particles. These particles, which are too small to be seen by the most powerful microscope, are called electrons and protons. The two particles differ from each other electrically and physically. Electrically, we say that the proton is positively charged while the electron is negatively charged. Physically, the proton is about 1800 times as heavy as the electron.

THE LAW OF ELECTRIC CHARGES

Most objects, such as a piece of wood, normally have a neutral or zero charge; that is, they contain as many electrons (negatively charged particles) as they do protons (positively charged particles). If this piece of wood can be made to have an excess of electrons, it would lose its neutral charge and become negatively charged. On the other hand, if the wood could be made to have a deficiency of electrons, the protons would predominate and it would become positively charged.

If we took a positively charged body and brought it near a negatively charged body, the two bodies would be drawn together. If, however, the two objects had the same charge (both positive or both negative), then they would repel each other. These two reactions form the basis of our first law of electricity - The Law Of Electric Charges. This law, which is illustrated in Figure 1-1, states that: "Like charges repel and unlike charges attract". In Figure 1-1A, a positively charged ball of cork is suspended by a piece of string near a negatively charged ball of cork. The two

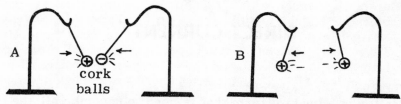

A.   Unlike charges attract   B.   Like charges repel

Figure 1-1.   Attraction and Repulsion.

bodies swing toward each other because they attract each other. Figure 1-1B illustrates two positively charged balls repelling each other.

DIFFERENCE OF POTENTIAL

If we were to connect a copper wire between the negative and the positive balls of cork, an electron flow would result. This is illustrated in Figure 1-2. The excess electrons from the negative ball flow to the positive ball where there is an electron deficiency and therefore, an attraction for the electrons.

This flow continues until the deficiency and excess of electrons has disappeared and the balls become neutral or uncharged. This flow of electrons between the two differently charged bodies is caused by the difference in charge. A difference in charge between two objects will always result in the development of an electrical pressure between them. It is this electrical pressure that causes the electrons to flow when these two bodies are connected by a piece of copper wire. This electrical pressure is defined as a DIFFERENCE OF POTENTIAL. The word "POTENTIAL" has the same meaning as the word "CHARGE".

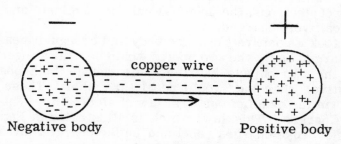

Figure 1-2.   Flow of electrons

CONDUCTORS AND INSULATORS

Materials through which current can easily flow are called CONDUCTORS. Most metals are good conductors. Conductors incorporate a large number of free electrons in their basic structure. These free electrons are not held tightly and will move freely through the conductor when stimulated by external electrical pressure. Examples of good conductors, in the order of their conductivity, are silver, copper, aluminum and zinc.

Those materials through which electrons flow with difficulty are called INSULATORS. The electrons are tightly held in the atomic structure of an insulator and therefore, cannot move about as freely as in conductors. Examples of insulators are wood, silk, glass and bakelite.

RESISTANCE

The ability of a material to oppose the flow of electrons is called RESISTANCE. All materials exhibit a certain amount of resistance to electron flow. In order to compare the resistances of various materials, we require some standard unit of resistance measurement. The unit of resistance that was adapted for this purpose is the OHM, and the Greek letter Omega (Ω) is its symbol. (For a list of common radio abbreviations, see Appendix 1). One ohm may be defined as the amount of resistance inherent in 1000 feet of #10 copper wire. For example, 5000 feet of #10 copper wire would have a resistance of 5 ohms; 10,000 feet of #10 copper wire would have 10 ohms, etc. Although the ohm is the basic unit, the MEGOHM, meaning 1,000,000 ohms, is frequently used. The instrument which is used to measure resistance is the OHMMETER.

There are four factors which determine the resistance of a conductor. They are:

(1) Length. The resistance of a conductor is directly proportional to its length. The longer the conductor, the greater is the resistance. The electrons have to flow through more material in a longer conductor and therefore, meet more opposition.

(2) Cross-sectional area. The resistance of a conductor is inversely proportional to the cross-sectional area. This means that the resistance becomes smaller as the thickness or area becomes larger. For example, if we double the cross-sectional area of a conductor of a given length, the resistance will be cut in half. If we triple the area, the resistance will be cut to one-third of its original resistance. The larger the cross-sectional area of a conductor, the easier it is for current to flow. If we decrease the cross-sectional area of the conductor, less electrons can squeeze

through.   Hence the conductor supplies a greater resistance.

(3) Temperature. In practically all conductors, with the exception of carbon, the resistance varies directly with the temperature. As the temperature of a conductor rises, its resistance increases; as the temperature drops, the resistance decreases.

(4) Material make-up. The resistance of a conductor depends upon the material of which it is made. Because of their material structure, some conductors have more resistance than others. For example, silver has a very low resistance, whereas nichrome has a high resistance.

RESISTORS

The resistor is a common radio part. Each resistor has a specific amount of resistance. Resistors which are made of mixtures of carbon and clay are called CARBON RESISTORS. Carbon resistors are used in low power circuits. Wire wound resistors, which contain special resistance wire, are used in high power circuits.   Figure 1-3 illustrates several types of fixed resistors which are used in radio circuits. The symbol which is used to represent them in circuit diagrams is also shown.

Fixed resistor symbol

High wattage wire-wound

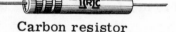

Carbon resistor   Precision resistor

Figure 1-3.   Fixed resistors.

When it becomes necessary to vary the amount of resistance in a circuit, we can use an ADJUSTABLE RESISTOR. The adjustable resistor has a sliding collar which may be moved along the resistance element to select any desired resistance value.

VARIABLE RESISTORS are used in a circuit when a resistance value must be changed frequently. Variable resistors are commonly called potentiometers or rheostats, depending on their use. The volume control in a radio is a typical example of a variable resistor. Figure 1-4B illustrates a potentiometer used as a volume control for a radio receiver. Figure 1-4C illustrates a potentiometer wound of heavier wire for use in a power supply circuit. Figure 1-4A illustrates a variable resistor which is used where frequent adjustment is not required.

A. Adjustable power resistor.

Variable resistor symbol.

B. Volume control potentiometer   C. Power supply rheostat.

Figure 1-4. Variable resistors.

CONDUCTANCE

The reciprocal or opposite of resistance is called CONDUCT-ANCE.

$$(1\text{-}1) \quad \text{conductance} = \frac{1}{\text{resistance}}$$

Conductance is the ability of an electrical circuit to pass or conduct electricity. A circuit having a large conductance has a low resistance; a circuit having a low conductance has a high resistance. The unit of conductance is the MHO. A resistance of one ohm has a conductance of one mho; a resistance of 10 ohms has a conductance of .1 mho (1/10 = 0.1). In other words, to determine the conductance, we divide the number 1 by the amount of the resistance in ohms. We frequently use the term MICROMHO, meaning one-millionth of a mho.

VOLTAGE AND CURRENT

Voltage is another term used to describe the difference of potential or electrical pressure which we spoke about in a preceding paragraph. It is the force which pushes or forces electrons through a wire, just as water pressure forces water through a pipe. Some other terms used to denote voltage are ELECTRO-MOTIVE FORCE (emf.), IR DROP and FALL OF POTENTIAL. The unit of voltage is the VOLT and the instrument used to measure voltage is the VOLTMETER. The KILOVOLT is equal to 1000 volts.

CURRENT is the term commonly used to describe the flow of electrons. It is the result of the application of a difference of potential to a circuit. If we increase the number of electrons flowing past a point in a given amount of time, we have more current. Conversely, if we decrease the number of electrons flowing past a point in a given amount of time, we decrease the current. The unit of current is the AMPERE and it is equal to 6, 280, 000, 000, -000, 000, 000 electrons flowing past a point in one second.

MILLIAMPERE and MICROAMPERE are terms used to denote one-thousandth and one-millionth of an ampere respectively. Current is measured by an AMMETER.

We have one more important term to define and that is the COULOMB. The coulomb is the unit of electrical quantity. The coulomb is the number of electrons contained in one ampere. One coulomb flowing past a point in one second is equal to one ampere. Many people confuse the COULOMB with the AMPERE. The difference is this: The ampere represents the RATE OF FLOW of a number of electrons, whereas the coulomb represents only the quantity of electrons and has nothing to do with the rate of flow or movement of the electrons. The coulomb is a unit that is seldom used in radio.

THE DRY CELL

There are several methods that are used to produce electricity. One of the most common methods is the dry cell that is found in a flashlight. The dry cell contains several chemicals combined to cause a chemical reaction which produces a voltage. The voltage produced by a new #6 dry cell is 1.53 volts, while that of a mercury cell is 1.34 volts. A battery is composed of a number of cells. Therefore, a battery may be 3 volts, 6 volts, 7-1/2 volts, etc., depending upon the number of cells it contains. The fact that a cell is larger than another one indicates that the larger cell is capable of delivering a given amount of current for a longer period of time than the smaller one. Figure 1-5 illustrates a typical 1-1/2 volt cell and a 45 volt battery. The 45 volt battery contains 30 small dry cells.

Fig. 1-5A. 1-1/2 v. flashlight cell.   Fig. 1-5B. 45 v. "B" battery.

Every cell has a negative and a positive terminal. The electrons leave the cell at the negative terminal, flow through the circuit and return to the cell at the positive terminal. This type of current flow is known as DIRECT CURRENT (DC). Direct current is current that flows only in ONE direction.

ELECTRICAL CIRCUITS

If we took a dry cell, two conductors and a bulb and hooked them up, as shown in Figure 1-6A, the bulb would light up. We would then have a complete electrical circuit. The heavy arrows in Figure 1-6A indicate the direction of the current flow. As long as we can trace the current from the negative point of the cell, all around the circuit and back to the positive point, we have a complete circuit. The important thing to remember is that current will only flow through a complete circuit.

The necessary parts for a complete circuit are:

(1) A source of voltage - the dry cell in Figure 1-6A.

(2) Connecting leads - the copper wire conductors in Figure 1-6A.

(3) A load - the bulb in Figure 1-6A.

If there were a break in the connecting leads or in the wire of the bulb, no current would flow and the light would go out. We

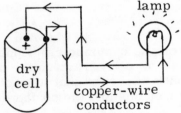

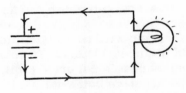

Fig. 1-6A Complete electrical circuit   Fig. 1-6B Schematic diagram

would then have an OPEN CIRCUIT. Figure 1-7A illustrates the open circuit condition.

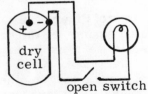

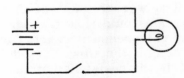

Fig. 1-7A. Open circuit.   Fig. 1-7B. Schematic diagram.

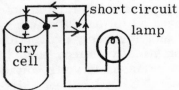

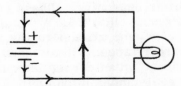

Fig. 1-8A. Short circuit.   Fig. 1-8B. Schematic diagram.

If we place a piece of wire directly across the two cell terminals, no current will flow through the bulb. This condition is illustrated in Figure 1-8A. The current by-passes the bulb and flows through the path of least resistance, which is the piece of wire. This condition is known as a SHORT CIRCUIT. It is to be avoided because it causes a severe current drain which rapidly wears the battery down.

SCHEMATICS

In drawing an electrical circuit on paper, we find it impractical to draw the actual battery or lamp, as was done in Figures 1-6A through 1-8A. Instead, we use simple symbols to represent the various electrical parts. For instance:

A cell is shown as ⊣⊢

A battery is shown as ⊣|ı||⊢

A resistor is shown as ⌐\/\/\⌐

You will find a complete table of radio symbols in Appendix 2. Figures 1-6A, 1-7A and 1-8A can now be redrawn in the manner shown in Figures 1-6B, 1-7B and 1-8B. Note that we indicate the negative battery terminal by a short line and the positive terminal by a long line.

OHM'S LAW

We have discussed the significance of voltage, current and resistance. Now we shall further study the important relationships that exist between these three factors.

If we were to increase the source voltage of Figure 1-6A, more electrons would flow through the circuit because of the greater electrical pressure exerted upon them. If we were to decrease the voltage, the flow of electrons would decrease. On the other hand, if the resistance of the circuit were made larger, the current would decrease because of greater opposition to current flow. If the resistance were made smaller, the current would increase by similar reasoning. These relationships are formulated into a law known as OHM'S LAW which is stated as follows: The current is directly proportional to the voltage and inversely proportional to the resistance. Ohm's law, mathematically stated, says that the current, in amperes, is equal to the voltage, in volts, divided by the resistance, in ohms.

The three formulas of Ohm's law are:

$$(1-2) \quad I = \frac{E}{R} \qquad (1-3) \quad E = IR \qquad (1-4) \quad R = \frac{E}{I}$$

"I" stands for current in amperes, "E" is the voltage in volts and "R" is the resistance in ohms. It is obvious that it is simpler to use letters such as I, E and R, than to actually write out the words. Also, note that IR means I multiplied by R. If two out of the three factors of Ohm's law are known (either E, I or R), the unknown third factor can be found by using one of the above three equations. Several examples will clarify the use of Ohm's law:

PROBLEM ONE

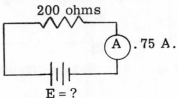

Given: Current is .75 amps.
        Resistance is 200 ohms.

Find: The voltage of the battery.

SOLUTION: Since we are interested in finding the voltage, we use formula 1-3 because it tells us what the voltage is equal to. We then substitute the known values and solve the problem as follows:

(1) E = IR
(2) E = .75 x 200
(3) E = 150 V.

$$\begin{array}{r} 200 \\ \times .75 \\ \hline 1000 \\ 1400 \\ \hline 150.00 \end{array}$$

PROBLEM TWO

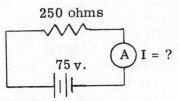

Given: Battery voltage is 75 volts.
        Resistance of bulb is 250 ohms.

Find: Current in circuit.

SOLUTION: Use formula 1-2 to find the current.

(1) $I = \frac{E}{R}$ (2) $I = \frac{75}{250}$ (3) I = .3 amp.

$$250 \overline{\smash{)}75.0} \quad .3 \\ 75\,0$$

PROBLEM THREE

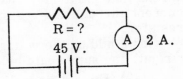

Given: Current in circuit is 2 amps.
        Battery voltage is 45 volts.

Find: Resistance of circuit.

SOLUTION: Use formula 1-4 and substitute E and I to find R.

(1) $R = \frac{E}{I}$ (2) $R = \frac{45}{2}$ (3) R = 22.5 ohms.

RESISTANCES IN SERIES

If two or more resistances are connected end to end, as shown in Figure 1-9A, we say that the resistors are hooked up in a SERIES CIRCUIT. Any current flowing through one of the resistors will also flow through the others. The arrows indicate the direction of current flow. Since the same current flows through

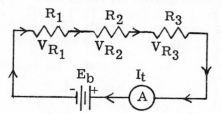

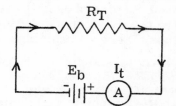

Fig. 1-9A. Series circuit.   Fig. 1-9B. Equivalent circuit

each resistor, the CURRENT IS THE SAME AT EVERY POINT IN A SERIES CIRCUIT. Similarly, the total current is the same as the current in any part of the series circuit. To put it mathematically:

$$(1\text{-}5) \quad I_{(total)} = I_{R_1} = I_{R_2} = I_{R_3}$$

It is important to note that the current in Figure 1-9A will remain unchanged if the separate series resistors are replaced by a single resistor whose resistance value is equal to the sum of the three resistors. Figure 1-9B illustrates the equivalent circuit of Figure 1-9A. We can therefore say that THE TOTAL RESISTANCE IN A SERIES CIRCUIT IS EQUAL TO THE SUM OF THE INDIVIDUAL RESISTANCES.

$$(1\text{-}6) \quad R_T = R_1 + R_2 + R_3, \text{ etc.} \text{ where } R_T \text{ is total resistance}$$

Whenever current flows through a resistance in a circuit, a part of the source voltage is used up in forcing the current to flow through the particular resistance. The voltage that is used up in this manner is known as the VOLTAGE DROP or fall of potential across that particular resistor. The voltage drop is equal to the current through the resistor, multiplied by the resistance of the resistor.

If we add up the voltage drops across all the parts of a series circuit, the sum would be equal to the source or battery voltage.

$$(1\text{-}7) \quad E_B = V_{R_1} + V_{R_2} + V_{R_3}, \text{ etc.}$$

where: E_B is the battery voltage, V_{R_1} is the voltage across R_1, V_{R_2} is the voltage across R_2, etc.

PROBLEM

Find the resistance of R_2
in Figure 1-10.

Fig. 1-10

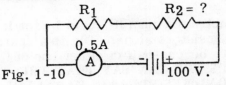

SOLUTION: (1) Since we know the total current and the battery voltage, we can use Ohm's law to find the total resistance.

(1) $R_T = \dfrac{E}{I} = \dfrac{100}{.5} = 200\,\Omega$

(2) Since the total resistance in this series circuit is 200 ohms and R = 75; then $R_2 = R_T - R_1$.

(3) $R_2 = 200 - 75$ (4) $R_2 = 125$ ohms.

RESISTANCES IN PARALLEL

The circuit in Figure 1-11A is called a PARALLEL CIRCUIT. R_1 and R_2 are in parallel with each other. The current in the circuit now has two paths to flow through from the negative end of the

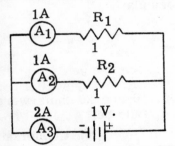

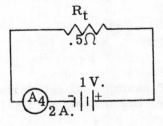

Fig. 1-11A. Parallel circuit   Fig. 1-11B. Equivalent circuit

battery to the positive end. If we remove resistor R_1 or R_2 from the circuit, the current has only one path to flow through from the negative to the positive end of the battery. Since it is easier for the current to flow through two paths instead of one, THE TOTAL RESISTANCE OF A PARALLEL COMBINATION IS LESS THAN THE RESISTANCE OF EITHER RESISTOR IN THE CIRCUIT. The more resistors we add in parallel, the less becomes the total resistance. This is because we increase the number of paths through which the current can flow. An analogy for this would be to consider the number of people that can pass through one door in a given time, compared to the number of people that can pass through several doors in the same time.

If each resistor in Figure 1-11A had a value of one ohm, it would be twice as easy for the current to pass through the parallel combination than it would be for it to pass through either one of the resistors alone. The total parallel resistance would, therefore, be one-half of either one of the resistors, or one-half ohm. THUS, WE CAN SAY THAT THE TOTAL RESISTANCE OF TWO EQUAL RESISTORS IN PARALLEL IS EQUAL TO ONE-HALF OF ONE OF THEM. Figure 1-11B shows the equivalent circuit of Figure 1-11A.

The total resistance of ANY TWO resistors in parallel may be found by using the following formula:

$$(1\text{-}8)\quad R_T = \frac{R_1 \times R_2}{R_1 + R_2}$$

For example, if R_1 and R_2 of Figure 1-11A were 3 and 6 ohms respectively, the total resistance would be:

(1) $R_T = \dfrac{R_1 \times R_2}{R_1 + R_2}$ (2) $R_T = \dfrac{3 \times 6}{3 + 6} = \dfrac{18}{9} = 2$ ohms

The total resistance of ANY NUMBER of resistors in parallel may be found by applying the following formula:

$$(1\text{-}9)\quad R_T = \frac{1}{\dfrac{1}{R_1} + \dfrac{1}{R_2} + \dfrac{1}{R_3}}\ \text{etc.}$$

For example, if three resistors of 5, 10 and 20 ohms were connected in parallel, the total resistance would be:

(1) $R_T = \dfrac{1}{\dfrac{1}{R_1} + \dfrac{1}{R_2} + \dfrac{1}{R_3}}$ (2) $R_T = \dfrac{1}{\dfrac{1}{5} + \dfrac{1}{10} + \dfrac{1}{20}}$ (least common denominator is 20)

(3) $\dfrac{1}{\dfrac{4 + 2 + 1}{20}} = \dfrac{1}{\dfrac{7}{20}}$ (4) $1 \times \dfrac{20}{7} = 2\dfrac{6}{7}$ ohms.

CHARACTERISTICS OF A PARALLEL CIRCUIT

(1) The total resistance of several resistors hooked in parallel is less than the smallest resistor.

(2) Different amounts of current flow through the different branches of a parallel circuit. The amount of current flowing through each branch depends upon the resistance of the individual branch. The total current drawn from the battery is equal to the

sum of the individual branch currents.

(3) The voltage across all the branches of a parallel circuit is the same; In Figure 1-11A, the voltage across R_1 is the same as the voltage across R_2.

An example will illustrate the above principles. Refer to Figure 1-12.

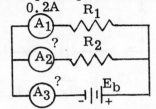

Given: Current through R_1 is .2A
R_1 = 50 ohms
R_2 = 200 ohms

Find: (1) Current through R_2.
(2) Total current.

Figure 1-12.

SOLUTION: Since we know the resistance of R_1 and the current through R_1, we can find the voltage across R_1 by using Ohm's law.

$$(1)\ E_{R_1} = I_{R_1} \times R_1 \quad (2)\ E_{R_1} = .2 \times 50 \quad (3)\ E_{R_1} = 10\ V.$$

Since R_1 is in parallel with R_2, the voltage across R_2 is the same as that across R_1. Therefore, $E_{R_2} = 10\ V$.

Knowing the resistance of R_2 (given) and the voltage across it, we can find the current through R_2:

$$I_{R_2} = \frac{E_{R_2}}{R_2} = \frac{10}{200} = .05\ \text{amp. (current through } R_2\text{)}$$

In a parallel circuit, the total current is equal to the sum of the individual branch currents; therefore:

$$(1)\ I_T = I_{R_1} + I_{R_2} \quad (2)\ I_T = .2A + .05A = .25\ \text{Amp.}$$
(total current)

SERIES-PARALLEL CIRCUITS

Circuits A and B of Figure 1-13 are called SERIES-PARAL-LEL circuits. In circuit A, the 10 ohm resistors are in parallel with each other. However, this parallel combination is in series with the 20 ohm resistor. The total resistance of circuit A is computed as follows:

First find the resistance of the two 10 ohm parallel resistors using formula 1-8.

$$R_T = \frac{R_1 \times R_2}{R_1 + R_2} = \frac{10 \times 10}{10 + 10} = \frac{100}{20} = 5\ \text{ohms.}$$

Since the parallel resistors are in series with the 20 ohm re-

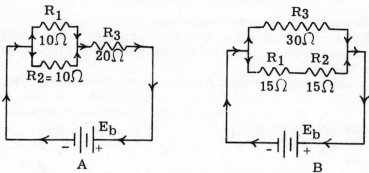

Fig. 1-13. Series-Parallel Circuits

sistor, then the total resistance of this combination is:

5 + 20 or 25 ohms.

In diagram B, the two 15 ohm resistors are in series with each other. The series combination is in parallel with the 30 ohm resistor. The total resistance of series-parallel circuit B is computed as follows:

The resistance of the two 15 ohm resistors in series is 15 + 15 or 30 ohms. Since this 30 ohms is in parallel with the 30 ohm resistor, the total resistance of the combination is:

$$R_T = \frac{30 \times 30}{30 + 30} = \frac{900}{60} = 15 \text{ ohms}$$

BRIDGE CIRCUITS

In Figure 1-14A, R_1 is in series with R_2 and R_3 is in series with R_4. The two combinations are in parallel with each other. While this grouping of resistors is recognized as a series-parallel circuit, it also represents the most elementary form of a "bridge" circuit. If we redraw the circuit slightly, adding a meter, as

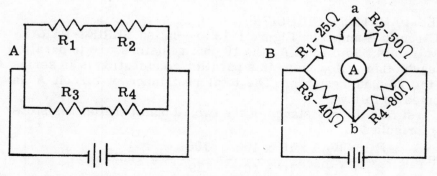

Figure 1-14. Forms of Wheatstone Bridges

shown in Figure 1-14B, we have what is commonly known as a "WHEATSTONE" bridge.

The resistance values chosen in Figure 1-14B are such that the ratio of R_1 to R_2 is the same as the ratio of R_3 to R_4. Because of this, the potential at point a is the same as that at point b and therefore, no current will flow between point a and point b. We have a balanced circuit. The relationship of the resistors under these conditions is shown by the following equation:

$$\frac{R_1}{R_2} = \frac{R_3}{R_4}$$

It is obvious that if we know the values of three of the resistors, we can find the fourth one by simply substituting the known values in the above equation and solving it. An example will show how this is done: Assume that R_1 is unknown and the other resistors have the values shown in Figure 1-14B.

$$\frac{R_1}{50} = \frac{40}{80} \qquad R_1 = \frac{40 \times 50}{80} = \frac{2000}{80} = 25 \text{ ohms.}$$

Thus, we see that a Wheatstone bridge can be used to accurately measure unknown resistance values.

POWER

Whenever current flows through a resistance, there is friction between the moving electrons and the particles of the resistor. This friction causes heat to be generated, as does all friction. We could also say that electrical energy is changed to heat energy whenever current flows through a resistor. The unit of energy is the JOULE. The rate at which the heat energy is generated is the power that the resistor consumes. This power consumption in the form of heat represents a loss because we do not make use of the heat generated in radio circuits.

We should know how much heat power a resistor is consuming or dissipating. This is important because a resistor will burn up if it cannot stand the heat that is being generated by current flow. Resistors are therefore rated, not only in ohms, but in the amount of power that they can dissipate without overheating. The unit of electrical power is the WATT. A resistor rated at 5 watts is one which can safely dissipate up to 5 watts of power. If this resistor is forced to dissipate 10 watts, by increased current flow, it will burn up. A KILOWATT is equal to 1,000 watts.

Let us see how much power is dissipated in a particular circuit and upon what factors the power dissipation depends. Since the power is the result of friction between the flowing electrons and the resistance in the circuit, the actual power dissipated depends upon the current and the resistance. The more current that flows, the more electrons there are to collide with the particles of the resistance material. Also, the greater the resistance, the greater is the resulting friction. The actual power dissipated in a resistor can be found by the following formula:

(1-10) $P = I^2 \times R$ where: P is the power in watts, I is the current in amperes and R is the resistance in ohms. (I^2 means I x I).

PROBLEM: Find the power dissipated in a 200 ohm resistor with 50 milliamperes flowing through it.

SOLUTION: First change milliamperes to amperes. This is done by moving the decimal three places to the left. Thus, 50 milliamperes = .05 amperes. Then substitute the values given in formula 1-10.

(1)	$P = I^2 \times R$	.05	.0025
(2)	P = .05 x .05 x 200	x .05	x 200
(3)	P = .5 watts	.0025	.5000

By using Ohm's law and algebraically substituting in formula 1-10, we can arrive at two more formulas for obtaining power dissipation.

(1-11) $P = E \times I$ (1-12) $P = \dfrac{E^2}{R}$

where: P is the power in watts, E is the voltage in volts, I is the current in amperes and R is the resistance in ohms.

Formula 1-11 states that the power is equal to the product of the voltage across the resistor and the current through the resistor.

Formula 1-12 enables us to calculate the power in watts if we know the voltage across a resistor (in volts) and the amount of resistance (in ohms). To use formula 1-12, multiply the voltage by itself (this is known as squaring the voltage) and then divide the answer by the resistance in ohms.

The WATTMETER is the instrument that is used to measure power.

POWER AND WORK

Power is generated or produced by huge AC generators which supply AC voltage and current to your home. The electric bills you pay are not only based on the power you use, but also on the length of time the power is used. Thus, we must make a distinction between power and work. Power is the rate of production of electrical energy. Work is power used per unit of time. Practical units of energy consumption are the watt-second, the watt-hour and the kilowatt-hour. The kilowatt-hour is the most commonly used unit. If, in your home, you use a toaster that requires one kilowatt, the electric bill you pay depends on how long you use that toaster. If you use the toaster for one hour, then you will be charged for one kilowatt-hour. The instrument that is used to measure energy is the WATT-HOUR METER.

CHAPTER 2

MAGNETISM AND METERS

THE MAGNET

We are all familiar with the effects of magnetism. A horse-shoe magnet will attract and pull to it iron filings. A powerful crane electromagnet will pick up heavy pieces of iron. A compass needle will point to the North pole. A magnet, therefore, is any object which has the ability of attracting to itself magnetic materials such as iron or steel. Figure 2-1 shows a horseshoe magnet attracting particles of iron filings.

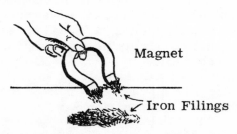

Magnet

Iron Filings

Figure 2-1. Magnet's attraction power.

When a magnetized bar of iron is suspended from a string tied around its center so that it is free to rotate, it will come to rest with one end pointing almost directly north. The end that points north is called the NORTH POLE, and the opposite end of the magnetized bar of iron is called the SOUTH POLE.

LAW OF MAGNETIC POLES

If the North pole end of one magnet is brought near the North pole end of another magnet, the magnets will repel each other. The same reaction of repulsion will occur if two South pole ends are brought close to each other. If, however, a North pole end and South pole end are brought close to each other, the magnets will attract each other. The reason that the North pole of a suspended magnet points to the earth's North geographical pole is that the earth itself is a magnet. The earth's South magnetic pole is located near the North geographical pole. The results of experiments in magnetic attraction and repulsion were formulated into the law of poles which states: OPPOSITE POLES ATTRACT EACH OTHER, WHEREAS LIKE POLES REPEL EACH OTHER. Figure 2-2 illustrates this principle.

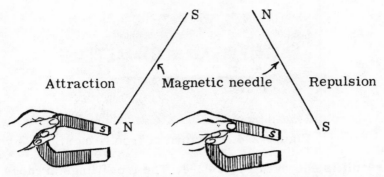

Figure 2-2. Attraction and repulsion.

MAGNETIC LINES OF FORCE

We cannot see the forces of repulsion or attraction that exist between the pole pieces of two magnets. However, we must assume that the North pole of one magnet sends out some kind of invisible force which has the ability to act through air and pull the South pole of the other magnet to it. If we had unique vision, we would be able to see certain lines leaving the North pole of one magnet and crossing over to the South pole of the other magnet. These lines are known as magnetic lines of force and, as a group, are called a MAGNETIC FIELD or FLUX. Figure 2-3 illustrates the magnetic field as it exists around a bar magnet. Notice that

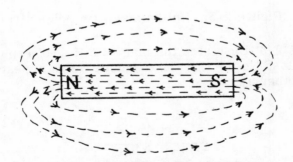

Figure 2-3. Magnetic Lines of Force

the lines of force leave the magnet at the North pole and return to the magnet at the South pole. Note, also, that the magnetic field continues flowing inside the magnet from the South to the North pole. The complete path of the magnetic flux is called the magnetic circuit.

One way to show magnetic lines of force is to sprinkle iron filings on a piece of paper under which we place a bar magnet.

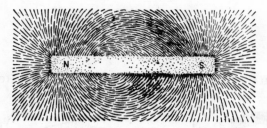

Figure 2-4.   Picture of iron filings.

The result is shown in Figure 2-4. The iron filings arrange themselves so as to look like the lines of force that surround the magnet.

Figure 2-5 illustrates the magnetic field of attraction as it exists between the North and South poles of two magnets. Notice that the magnetic field appears to be "pulling" the two pole ends together.

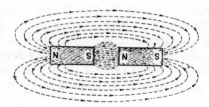

Figure 2-5.   Unlike magnetic poles attract.

Figure 2-6 illustrates the magnetic field of repulsion between two like poles. Notice that the magnetic fields appear to be "pushing" each other away.

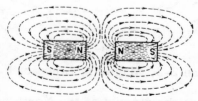

Figure 2-6.   Like magnetic poles repel.

THE MAGNETIC CIRCUIT

Magnetic flux flowing in a magnetic circuit is similar to electric current flowing in an electrical circuit. The magnetic flux has a direction of flow, as well as a given strength or amplitude.

Just as a current will flow only when the electrical circuit is complete, similarly, a magnetic flux can exist only if there exists a complete magnetic path.

SHIELDING

If a non-magnetic object, such as a tennis ball, were placed in the path of a magnetic field, as shown in Fig. 2-7, the lines of force would pass right through the ball, just as the light shines through a piece of glass. However, if the tennis ball were covered up with a thick layer of soft iron, the lines of force would flow through the soft iron and not through the center of the ball. The reason for this is that the soft iron offers much less resistance to the magnetic flux than the air does. This is illustrated in Figure 2-8. Notice that the area in the center of the ball is now free of magnetic flux. The above example illustrates the principle of magnetic shielding which is so extensively used in electronic circuits.

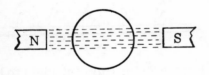

Figure 2-7. No shielding.   Figure 2-8. Shielding.

People who work near strong magnetic fields usually encase their watches in soft iron through which the magnetic field will not penetrate. The delicate watch movement is therefore protected and will not be adversely affected by the magnetic field.

TEMPORARY AND PERMANENT MAGNETS

Soft iron can be magnetized easily by placing it in a magnetic field. However, as soon as the iron is removed from the magnetic field, it loses its magnetism. Such a magnet is called a TEMPORARY MAGNET. Steel or hard iron, on the other hand, which is difficult to magnetize, retains its magnetism after it has been removed from the magnetic field. A magnet of this type is called a PERMANENT MAGNET. Permanent magnets are usually made in the shape of a bar or a horse-shoe. The horse-shoe type has the stronger magnetic field because the magnetic poles are closer to each other.

RESIDUAL MAGNETISM

We stated above that a temporary magnet loses its magnetism

when it is removed from a magnetic field. This is not entirely true because a small amount of magnetism does remain. This small amount is called the **RESIDUAL MAGNETISM**. Its importance will become apparent when we study the subject of generators.

ELECTROMAGNETISM

The same type of magnetic field that we have been discussing, exists around all wires carrying current. This can be proven by placing a compass next to a current-carrying conductor. It will be found that the compass needle will turn until it is at right angles to the conductor. Since a compass needle lines up in the direction of the magnetic field, the field must exist in a plane at right angles to the conductor. Figure 2-9 illustrates a current-carrying conductor with its associated magnetic field. The current flows from left to right and the magnetic field is in the direction shown by the arrows. In Figure 2-10, the current flows from right to left and

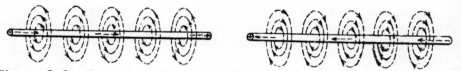

Figure 2-9. Current left to right.   Figure 2-10. Current right to left.

the magnetic field is in the opposite direction. This magnetic field, of which only a number of cross-sections are shown, encircles the wire all along its length like a cylinder. Notice that the direction of the magnetic field, as indicated by the arrows, depends upon the direction of the current flow in the wire.

THE COIL

If the same conductor is wound in the form of a coil, the total magnetic field about the coil will be greatly increased because the magnetic fields of each turn add up to make one large resultant magnetic field. See Figure 2-11. The coil is called a SOLENOID or ELECTROMAGNET. The electromagnet has a North and South pole, just like a permanent magnet. The rule for determining which end is the North pole and which end is the South pole is as follows: If we grasp the coil with the left hand so that the finger tips point in the direction of the current flow, the thumb will automatically point to the North pole of the electromagnet. Thus, we see that the polarity of an electromagnet depends upon both the way in which the turns are wound and the direction of the current flow. If we reverse either the direction of the current flow or the direction of the windings, the North pole will become the South

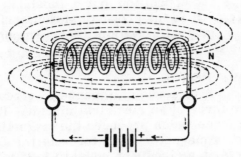

Figure 2-11. Magnetic field produced by current
flowing through coil of wire or solenoid.

pole and the South pole will become the North pole.

A compass, placed within the coil carrying an electric current, will point to the North pole of the coil. The reason for this
is that the compass needle lines itself up in the direction of the
magnetic lines of force. You will recall that inside a magnet, the
direction of the field is from the South pole to the North pole. This
is also true in the electromagnet illustrated in Figure 2-11.

There are various factors which influence the strength of an
electromagnet. They are:

(1) The number of turns. An increase in the number of turns
in a coil increases the magnetic strength of the coil.

(2) The amount of current. If we increase the amount of current in a coil, the magnetic strength increases.

(3) Permeability of the core. The core of the coil is the material within the coil. It may be air, glass, wood or metal. If we
wind the coil on an iron core, we find that the strength of the electromagnet is increased by several hundred times over what it is
with an air core. The iron is said to have more permeability than
air. PERMEABILITY is the ability of a substance to conduct magnetic lines of force easily. Permeability is to a magnetic circuit
as conductance is to an electrical circuit. If we have a core with
a high permeability, we will have a large number of magnetic lines
of force. This will result in a stronger magnetic field. Iron and
Permalloy are examples of materials having high permeability.
Air is arbitrarily given a permeability of "one". The permeability
of air is the basis for comparing the permeability of other materials. Iron and steel, for example, have a permeability of several
hundred.

RELUCTANCE

Magnetic reluctance is similar to electrical resistance. Magnetic reluctance is the opposition that a substance offers to magnetic lines of force. It is the property of a material that opposes the creation of a magnetic flux within itself. The unit of reluctance is the REL or the OERSTED.

MAGNETOMOTIVE FORCE

The magnetomotive force of a magnetic circuit is similar to the electromotive force of an electrical circuit. The magnetomotive force is the force which produces the magnetic lines of force or flux. The unit of magnetomotive force is the GILBERT. The number of gilberts in a circuit is equal to 1.26 x N x I, where N is the number of turns in the coil and I is the number of amperes. N x I, alone, is also known by the term AMPERE-TURNS. It is the number of turns, multiplied by the number of amperes flowing in the circuit.

INDUCED VOLTAGE

If a coil of wire is made to cut a magnetic field, a voltage is induced in the coil of wire. The same reaction will occur if the magnetic field cuts the coil of wire. In other words, as long as there is relative motion between a conductor and a magnetic field, a voltage will be generated in the conductor. An induced voltage is sometimes called an induced emf. (emf. is the abbreviation for electromotive force).

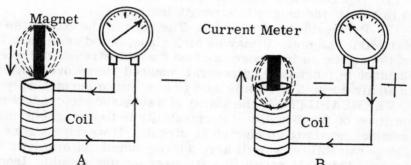

A. Magnet moving into coil.   B. Magnet moving out of coil.
Figure 2-12. Inducing a voltage in a coil of wire.

Figure 2-12A shows an iron bar magnet being thrust into a coil of wire. The dotted lines about the magnet represent magnetic lines of force. The relative movement between the coil and magnet will result in turns of wire of the coil cutting the lines of force of the magnetic field. The net result of this action will be an induced voltage generated in the turns of the coil. This induced voltage will, in turn, cause a current to flow in the coil. A galvanometer (an instrument used to detect the presence of small currents) will deflect to the right, indicating a current flow as a result of the induced emf. Figure 2-12B shows the magnet being pulled out of the coil. The galvanometer needle will now deflect to the left, indicating that the current is now in the opposite direction. Reversing the direction of the motion of the magnet, in relation to the coil, reverses the direction of the induced emf. This is indicated in Figure 2-12B by the position of the galvanometer needle.

This method of electromagnetic induction is used in the generators which supply us with our electricity. If we wish to increase the strength of the induced emf., we can do the following:

(1) Use a stronger magnet.

(2) Use more turns on the coil.

(3) Move the magnet or the coil back and forth at a faster rate.

(4) Have the coil cut the lines of force at right angles, if it is not already doing so. In other words, the more lines of force cut per second, the stronger is the resultant induced emf.

In order to determine the direction in which the induced current will flow, we use LENZ'S LAW. Lenz's law states that: when a moving magnetic field induces an emf. in a coil, a current will flow in such a direction as to form a magnetic field within the coil which will oppose the motion of the original magnetic field.

METERS

There are many different types of meters and instruments used in the electronics field. However, the most common meters are the voltmeter, the ammeter and the ohmmeter. While the function of each of these meters is different, they all make use of a basic meter movement known as the d'Arsonval type of meter movement. We shall now discuss this movement, as well as the three different meters.

D'ARSONVAL MOVEMENT

The d'Arsonval type of meter movement makes use of the principle of magnetic attraction and repulsion that has been described earlier in this chapter. A simplified illustration of the d'Arsonval movement is shown in Figure 2-13. A coil of fine wire is suspended by two spiral springs in a magnetic field created by a permanent horseshoe magnet. A pointer is attached to the coil. If current flows through the coil, a magnetic field will be set up

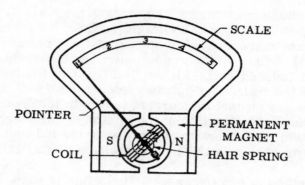

Figure 2-13 The D'Arsonval type of meter movement.

around the coil that will react with the field of the permanent magnet. If the current flows through the coil in the direction of the
arrows, the left hand side of the coil will become a South magnetic
pole and the right hand side will become a North magnetic pole.
This will cause the coil to rotate in a clockwise direction (the South
pole of the coil moves toward the North pole of the permanent
magnet). The spiral springs at the ends of the coil (in Figure 2-13
only one spring is shown - the other is hidden by the coil) tend to
keep the coil from rotating. The magnetic reaction between the
coil and the permanent magnet overcomes this resistance of the
springs. If we increase the current through the coil, the coil will
rotate more. This is due to the increased magnetic reaction between the permanent magnet and the stronger field of the coil.
When the current through the coil is removed, the two springs
force the coil to return to its original position. The pointer that
is attached to the coil deflects across a scale, thereby indicating
relative amounts of current that flow through the movement.
    If the d'Arsonval meter movement is used alone as an instru-
ment, it is called a galvanometer. The galvanometer merely indicates the presence of current; its scale is not calibrated to read
amperes or volts.

THE AMMETER
    In order to convert the d'Arsonval meter movement to an am-
meter, we must add a SHUNT to it. A shunt is a very low value of
resistance that is connected parallel to the meter movement. This
is shown in Figure 2-14. The current that enters the ammeter
divides itself into two paths at point A. Because the shunt has a
much lower resistance than the meter movement, most of the cur-

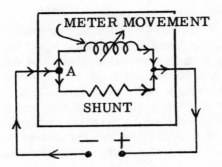

Fig. 2-14.   The ammeter.

rent flows through the shunt. Only a small amount of current flows through the meter movement. This is done because the meter movement is made up of very thin wire and would burn up if too much current flowed through it. The scale is calibrated so that it reads the total current flowing through both the meter movement and the shunt. The ammeter is always hooked up in series with the circuit that it is measuring. An ammeter that is used to measure current in the order of milliamperes is called a milliammeter.

VOLTMETER

By adding a high resistance in series with the basic meter movement, we convert it to a voltmeter. This is shown in Figure 2-15. The high resistance is called a multiplier and it limits the flow of current through the delicate meter movement. We know exactly how much voltage at the voltmeter's terminals will cause a certain amount of current to flow through the meter movement. We can, therefore, accurately calibrate the scale in volts. A voltmeter is always hooked in parallel to the part across which it is measuring the voltage.

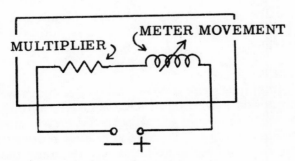

Fig. 2-15.   The voltmeter.

OHMMETER

Figure 2-16 illustrates the basic ohmmeter. Unlike the voltmeter and ammeter, a source of voltage is required for the ohmmeter. We use a small dry cell battery for this. The battery is in series with the meter movement and the unknown resistance. As we place different amounts of resistance across the ohmmeter terminals, we get different amounts of current flowing through the meter. Although the meter is actually reading current flow, the various amounts of current are the results of the different resistances measured by the ohmmeter. The scale is, therefore, calibrated in ohms.

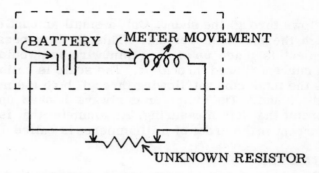

Figure 2-16. The ohmmeter.

CHAPTER 3

ALTERNATING CURRENT THEORY

INTRODUCTION

Chapter 1 deals with DC current -- current that flows in one direction only. In this chapter, we will study a type of current that periodically reverses its direction of flow. This type of current is called ALTERNATING CURRENT (abbreviated AC). A popular method of producing Direct Current is by means of a battery; Alternating Current is produced by means of an AC generator.

DEVELOPMENT OF THE ALTERNATING CURRENT WAVE

Let us see how we can develop or generate Alternating Current. Figure 3-1 illustrates a loop of wire which can be rotated between the poles of a magnet. (The magnetic field that exists between the North and South poles is not shown in the diagram).

If the loop of wire is rotated through the magnetic field, an electromotive force or voltage will be induced in the wire of the loop. This is because a conductor is cutting a magnetic field and

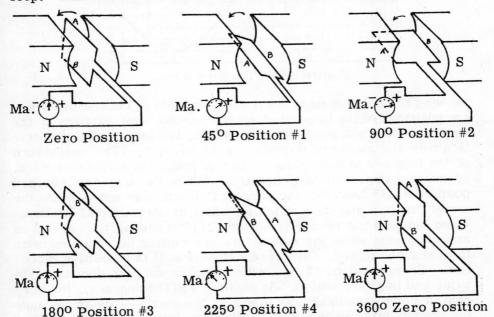

Figure 3-1. Generating the alternating current sine wave.

33

whenever this happens, a voltage is induced in the conductor.

The voltage developed in the loop of wire will cause a flow of current. The milliammeter, in series with the loop, will indicate this current flow.

One of the factors influencing the strength of the induced emf. is the relative cutting position of the loop, as compared to the direction of the magnetic field. When the conductors of the loop cut perpendicular to the magnetic field, a maximum induced voltage will be generated. When the conductors of the loop are moving parallel to the magnetic field, no lines of force will be cut and, therefore, no voltage will be generated. If the loop is rotated at a constant speed in a counter-clockwise direction, a current will flow whose strength and direction will vary with different positions of the loop. The strength and direction of the current for different loop positions are indicated in Figure 3-1. Figure 3-2 is a graph

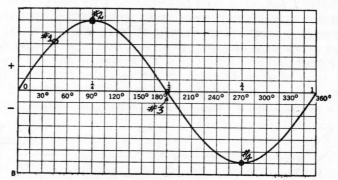

Figure 3-2. The sine wave.

showing the relationship between the amounts of current at different positions of the loop. Let us see exactly what happens at the various loop positions. At zero position, the loop begins its rotation with the ammeter indicating zero current. (The conductors of the loop are moving parallel to the magnetic lines; therefore, no induced emf. will be generated). When the loop has reached position #1 (45 degrees), the current flow which is indicated on the meter, is in a direction which we shall arbitrarily call positive. When the loop has reached position #2 (90 degrees), the current is at a maximum since the conductors are cutting into the magnetic field at right angles. The current flow is still in a positive direction. From position #2 to position #3, the current decreases in value and is still positive. At position #3 (180 degrees), the current is zero once again, as it was at the start. This is because the conductor is moving parallel with the magnetic field, but is not actually cutting it.   From position #3, through #4 and back to the starting position, the current goes through the same changes as it has gone through from starting position (zero degrees) to position #3 (180 degrees). However, from position #3 to zero position, the direction of the current has reversed itself and is now considered negative. This is because the loop of wire is now cutting the magnetic field in the opposite direction. The opposite of positive is negative and this is shown on the graph by drawing the curve below the horizontal center line. The curve of Figure 3-2, representing the varying current through the loop, is a waveform known as the ALTERNATING CURRENT wave. The mathematical name for a fundamental alternating current wave is a SINE WAVE.

The action just described is the basis for the alternating current generators that supply us with our electricity. Instead of one loop of wire, there are many turns of wire that are rotated through strong magnetic fields.

TO SUMMARIZE: ALTERNATING CURRENT, AS OPPOSED TO DIRECT CURRENT, CONTINUOUSLY VARIES IN STRENGTH (OR AMPLITUDE) AND PERIODICALLY REVERSES ITS DIRECTION OF FLOW.

CHARACTERISTICS OF THE SINE WAVE

A sine wave has the following important characteristics:

(1) The complete wave, as shown in Figure 3-3, is known as a CYCLE.   The wave is generated in one complete revolution of the loop from 0 to 360 degrees.

(2) An alternation is one-half cycle, from 0° to 180°, or from 180° to 360°.

(3) The frequency of a sine wave is the number of complete cycles in one second. Assuming that the sine wave of Figure 3-3 takes one second from 0° to 360°, then we have a frequency of one cycle per second. If 60 such cycles were completed in one second, the frequency would be 60 cycles per second.   The time taken for

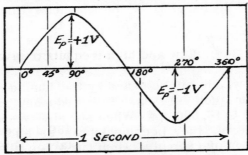

Figure 3-3.   The sine wave.

one such cycle would be 1/60th of a second.

(4) The height of the wave at any point is known as its AMPLI-TUDE. The highest point of the wave is called the maximum or PEAK AMPLITUDE, which, in Figure 3-3, is one volt. In a sine wave, the peaks always occur at 90 degrees and 270 degrees; the zero points always occur at 0, 180 and 360 degrees.

FREQUENCY

The unit of frequency is cycles per second, or simply cycles. The abbreviation for cycles per second is CPS. The word Hertz (abbreviated Hz) is also used to represent cycles per second.

The frequency of the AC power that is supplied to most homes in the United States today is 60 cycles per second. This is known as the POWER FREQUENCY. Radio waves transmitted by radio stations have a much higher frequency than the 60 cps. power frequency; they are usually above 400, 000 cps. The abbreviation for radio frequency is RF. Figure 3-4 illustrates a low frequency of 60 cps (60 Hz) and a high frequency of 1, 000, 000 cps. (1, 000, 000 Hz).

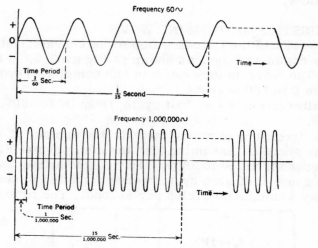

Figure 3-4. Low and high frequency wave.

Sound waves which can be heard by the human ear are called audible sounds, or audio sounds. The frequency range of audio sounds is from 16 to 16, 000 cps. When sound waves are converted into electrical waves, they become known as audio frequencies (abbreviated AF). For example, when our voice is amplified by a public address system, the sound waves from our throats strike the microphone and are converted into electrical frequencies in the audio range.

Higher frequencies are generally expressed in kilocycles or megacycles. A kilocycle (kc. or kHz.) is equal to 1,000 cycles. The prefix "kilo" stands for one thousand. In order to convert cycles to kilocycles, we divide the number of cycles by 1,000.

For example: $25,000 \text{ cps.} = \dfrac{25,000}{1,000} = 25 \text{ kc.}$

A megacycle (Mc. or MHz.) is equal to 1,000,000 cycles. The prefix "meg" stands for one million. In order to convert cycles into megacycles, we divide the number of cycles by a million.

For example: $4,000,000 \text{ cps.} = \dfrac{4,000,000}{1,000,000} = 4 \text{ Mc.}$

THE MEANING OF PHASE RELATIONSHIP

If two alternating current generators are connected in series across a load, and if their armatures are started rotating together from exactly the same point, two emf.'s will be produced. Let us assume that the peak output of generator #1 is 7 volts and the peak output of generator #2 is 5 volts. Since both generators start from the same position, at the same time and at the same speed, they will both produce the maximum and minimum voltages at the same instant. This is illustrated in Figure 3-5. Because the maximums and minimums of the two waves occur at the same time, we say that they are IN PHASE WITH EACH OTHER. Being in phase, the voltages become additive. Therefore, the resultant peak will be neither 7 volts nor 5 volts, but 12 volts, the combination of the two.

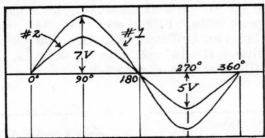

Figure 3-5. In phase.

Now, let us assume that generator #2 is started an eighth of a revolution (45 degrees) after generator #1 has started. The output of the two generators will reach maximum and minimum points at different times. They will now be OUT OF PHASE, as shown in Figure 3-6. It should be observed that the same voltages are be-

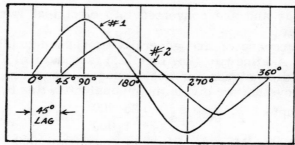

Figure 3-6.   Out of phase.

ing considered here as in Figure 3-5, but that the 5 volt wave LAGS 45° behind the 7 volt wave. These waves are said to be out of phase by 45°. If the 5 volt wave had started 90° later than the other, the 5 volt wave would be lagging the 7 volt wave by 90°. The angle by which one wave leads or lags another wave is known as the PHASE ANGLE.

EFFECTIVE VALUE OF AN AC WAVE

Let us consider a DC voltage of 100 volts and an AC wave whose peak is 100 volts (see Figure 3-7). We can see that the DC voltage is really peak voltage at all times; that is, it remains constant. The AC wave reaches its peak value only for a fraction of each cycle. If we connect a lamp, first to the DC voltage and then to the AC, the lamp will light up more brilliantly when connected to the DC. This is because the DC voltage remains at 100 volts continuously, whereas the AC voltage reaches a 100 volt peak only at two points during the cycle. In order for the lamp to light with equal brilliance on AC as well as on DC, we must raise the AC voltage to 141 peak volts. Effectively then, 141 peak volts of AC will light up a lamp as brilliantly as does 100 volts of DC. The EFFECTIVE value of the 141 volt peak AC wave is, therefore, 100 volts. This is illustrated in Figure 3-8.

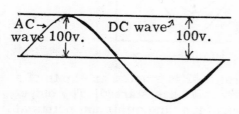

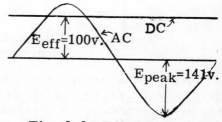

Fig. 3-7. DC wave equals peak of AC wave

Fig. 3-8. Effective value of a sine wave.

The effective value of an AC wave (either voltage or current) is 0.707 times its peak value. For example, the effective value of the above AC wave is 0.707 x 141 volts or 100 volts, which is also the value of the DC wave. The magnitude of an AC wave is usually given by its effective value from which the peak value can be calculated to be 1.41 x the effective value. The effective voltage or current is frequently referred to as the rms. (root-mean-square) value.

CALCULATION OF PEAK AND EFFECTIVE VALUE

The peak value of an AC wave can be calculated from its effective value by using the following formula:

(3-1) $E_{peak} = 1.41 \times E_{eff}$

The effective value of an AC wave can be calculated from the peak value by using the following formula:

(3-2) $E_{eff} = 0.707 \times E_{peak}$

Formulas 3-1 and 3-2 apply for all sine waves, whether voltage or current.

The value given to an AC wave will always be the effective value, unless otherwise stated. AC voltmeters and ammeters will always read the effective value of the AC wave, unless it is otherwise indicated.

INDUCTANCE

In a previous paragraph, we learned that a current-carrying coil of many turns behaves just like a magnet. The current will cause a magnetic field to surround the coil. If the current flowing through the coil is alternating, the magnetic field surrounding the coil will also be alternating. In Figure 3-9, we have a coil which has an alternating current flowing through it. This alternating current produces an alternating magnetic field around the coil

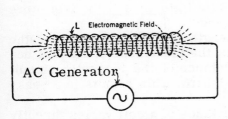

Fig. 3-9 Coil with AC
flowing through it.

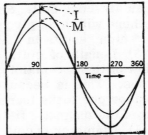

Fig. 3-10 Current wave and
magnetic field in phase.

which expands and collapses in step (or in phase) with the alternating current. When the current is zero, the magnetic field is zero; when the current reaches its peak at 90°, the magnetic field reaches its maximum value. This is shown in Figure 3-10. Since the field starts from zero and builds up to a maximum, it is an expanding field. This expanding field must cut through the conductors of the coil itself. According to Lenz's law, the cutting action induces an emf. in the coil which opposes the original current. In other words, alternating current flowing through a coil induces a voltage into the coil that is in opposition to the original voltage. The process wherein an induced emf. is generated in a coil is called SELF-INDUCTION. The coil of wire is called an INDUCTANCE. The unit of inductance is the HENRY and the abbreviation of henry is h. The symbol for inductance is L. Smaller and more practical units of inductance are the millihenry (mh.) and the microhenry (μh.).

$$1 \text{ millihenry} = \frac{1}{1000} \text{ of a henry}$$

$$1 \text{ microhenry} = \frac{1}{1,000,000} \text{ of a henry}$$

FACTORS AFFECTING THE INDUCTANCE OF A COIL

(1) Number of turns. The inductance of a coil varies as the square of the number of turns. For example, if we have two coils of the same length and diameter and coil #1 has four turns, while coil #2 has eight turns, the inductance of coil #2 will be four times the inductance of coil #1.

$$\frac{L_2}{L_1} = \frac{8^2}{4^2} = \frac{64}{16} = \frac{4}{1} ; \ L_2 = 4 \times L_1$$

(2) Core material. The inductance of a coil varies with the core material. An iron-core coil will have a higher inductance than an air-core coil. Since iron has a higher permeability than air, there will be a stronger magnetic field around the iron-core coil, which results in a high inductance.

(3) Length of coil. As the length of a coil increases, the number of turns remaining constant, the inductance of the coil decreases. This is because the reluctance of the magnetic circuit increases due to the increased coil length. This results in a weakening of the magnetic field.

(4) Diameter of coil. The inductance of a coil varies directly as the square of the diameter. For example, if we double the diameter of a coil, the inductance will increase four times.

INDUCTIVE REACTANCE

Due to the counter-electromotive force of self-induction, an inductance resists a change of current flow. This resistance or holding-back effect is measured in ohms. Instead of being called a resistance, however, it is called a reactance; an INDUCTIVE REACTANCE. The symbol for inductive reactance is X_L.

The formula for computing inductive reactance is:

(3-3) $X_L = 2\pi fL$ where: the symbol π is 3.14,
f = frequency of the applied voltage in cps.
L = inductance of the coil in henries.

(If the inductance is given in mh or μh, it must first be converted into henries before it can be used in formula 3-3.

PROBLEM: Find the inductive reactance of a 10 millihenry coil at a frequency of 60 cycles per second.

SOLUTION: First convert 10 mh to h; then use formula 3-3.

(1) $10 \text{ mh} = \dfrac{10}{1000} \text{ h} = \dfrac{1}{100}\text{h}$ (2) $X_L = 2\pi fL$

(3) $2 \times 3.14 \times 60 \times \dfrac{1}{100} = 3.768$ ohms.

PHASE ANGLE IN AN INDUCTIVE CIRCUIT

If AC is applied to an ordinary resistive circuit, the voltage and current are in phase with one another. However, this is not true if AC is applied to an inductive circuit. If we apply AC to a "pure" inductive circuit (one that contains only inductance and no resistance), the current will lag the impressed voltage by 90°. This is illustrated in Figure 3-11. The waveform E starts 90° ahead of the waveform I. We say that the phase angle between the voltage and current is 90°. Since, in actual practice, a coil or inductance will always have some resistance (the resistance of the

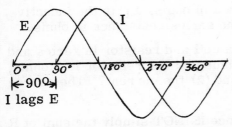

Fig. 3-11. Pure inductive circuit.

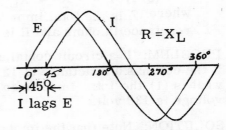

Fig. 3-12. Inductive-resistive circuit.

wire), the phase angle between the impressed emf. and the current becomes less than 90º. The greater the proportion of resistance, the smaller will be the phase angle. Figure 3-12 illustrates the current lagging the impressed voltage by 45º in a circuit containing equal amounts of resistance and inductive reactance. When there is all resistance and no inductance, the phase angle becomes 0 degrees. The current and voltage are then in phase. This is to be expected, since it is the counter emf. of the inductance which causes the current to lag.

IMPEDANCE OF AN INDUCTIVE CIRCUIT

In Figure 3-13A, the total resistance which opposes the flow of current is $R_1 + R_2$. The total resistance to current flow in a series circuit is the sum total of the individual resistances. If the circuit consists of resistance and inductive reactance, as shown in Figure 3-13B, the total resistance to the flow of current is called the IMPEDANCE. The symbol for impedance is Z. The

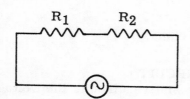

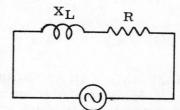

Fig. 3-13A. Resistive circuit   Fig. 3-13B. Inductive-
resistive circuit.

unit of impedance is the ohm. Unlike a resistive circuit, the impedance of an inductive circuit is NOT equal to the simple sum of the resistance and the inductive reactance. The impedance of an inductive circuit can be calculated by using the following formula:

$$(3-4) \quad Z = \sqrt{R^2 + X_L^2} \text{ ohms}$$

where: Z is the total impedance in ohms, X_L is the inductive reactance in ohms and R is the series resistance in ohms.

PROBLEM: If a circuit contains a coil and resistor in series and if the coil has a reactance of 12 ohms and the resistor is 5 ohms, what is (1) the total impedance and (2) the current? The source voltage is 130 volts.

SOLUTION: Note that the impedance IS NOT simply the sum of R and X_L, or 17 ohms. The impedance in an INDUCTIVE CIRCUIT must be calculated by using formula 3-4.

(1) $Z = \sqrt{R^2 + X_L^2}$

(2) $\sqrt{5^2 + 12^2} = \sqrt{25 + 144} = \sqrt{169}$

(3) $Z = 13$ ohms.

The current in the circuit is simply the total voltage divided by the impedance. This is in accordance with Ohm's law.

$$I = \frac{E}{Z} = \frac{130}{13} = 10 \text{ amperes}$$

THE CAPACITOR

We have thus far studied two radio parts which exert a limiting effect upon current: (1) resistors and (2) coils or inductors (which exert a limiting effect upon AC only). We shall now investigate another limiting device which has a tremendous application in radio - the CAPACITOR.

A capacitor is a device having, in its simplest form, two conducting plates, separated from each other by an insulator. This insulator is called a DIELECTRIC. The dielectric may be air, mica, oil, paraffined paper, etc. Figure 3-14 illustrates a two-plate capacitor connected across a battery. When the switch is closed, a certain number of free electrons on plate A will be attracted to the positive side of the battery. Plate A will, therefore, be left with a positive charge. At the same time, plate B will have the same number of electrons pushed on to it by the negative side of the battery. This electron flow continues until a charge is built up on the capacitor plates which develop a voltage equal to the battery voltage. The plates of the capacitor are now said to be electrically charged. The charge on the capacitor plates depends upon the size of the plates (the capacity) and the force of the battery, (the emf.). Notice that the accumulated electrons on plate B can-

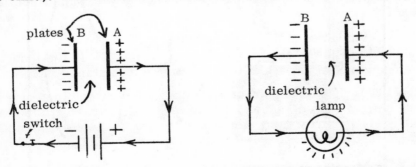

Fig. 3-14 Charging the capacitor. Fig. 3-15 Capacitor discharge.

not cross to the other plate because of the insulator dielectric between them.

When the capacitor has become fully charged, the voltage across the capacitor is equal to the battery voltage. If we disconnect the battery from the capacitor, the capacitor will continue to hold its charge. If a lamp is now connected across the charged capacitor (see Figure 3-15), the excess electrons on plate B will flow through the lamp and onto positive plate A. This is because electrons are attracted to a positively charged body. During the brief duration of the electron flow, the lamp will light for an instant, indicating that a current is passing through it. The electrons will continue to flow until plate B no longer has a surplus of electrons. Plate B is then said to have a zero charge. Plate B is now neutral and of course, plate A will have regained its electrons so that is is also neutral. The capacitor is now said to be discharged. A capacitor, then, is a device in which electricity may be stored for a period of time.

CAPACITANCE

The capacitance of a capacitor is determined by the following factors: The surface area of the plates, the number of plates, the spacing between plates and the type of dielectric used.

The symbol for capacitance is C. The unit of capacitance is the FARAD; the abbreviation for farad is fd. or f. Since the farad is an extremely large unit of capacitance, it is very rarely used. The more common, smaller units of capacitance are the micro-

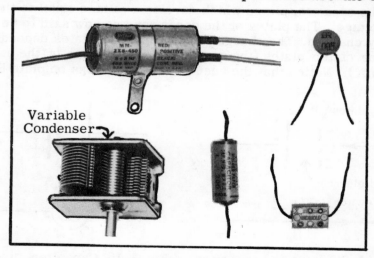

Variable
Condenser

Fig. 3-16. Various types of condensers used in radio.

farad and the micromicrofarad. The symbol for microfarad is μfd. or μf.; the symbol for micromicrofarad is $\mu\mu$fd. or $\mu\mu$f. In recent years, the term "picofarad" has replaced the term "microfarad". Its abbreviation is pfd. or pf.

$$1\,\mu f. = \frac{1}{1,000,000}\ fd. \qquad 1\ pf. = \frac{1}{1,000,000,000,000}\ fd.$$

The range of capacitors used in radio work may vary all the way from 5 pfd. to 100 μfd. Figure 3-16 illustrates several different types of capacitors used in radio work.

THE DIELECTRIC

The dielectric is nothing more than the name for the insulating material between the plates of a capacitor. Examples of dielectrics used in capacitors are mica, ceramic, glass, oil, waxpaper, etc. Capacitors with different dielectric materials will have different capacities. For example, a capacitor with a mica dielectric will have a larger capacity than an air dielectric capacitor of similar dimensions. The dielectric determines the ability of a capacitor to hold more or less charge.

THE VARIABLE CAPACITOR

Figure 3-17 shows the schematic symbol of a capacitor whose capacity can be varied. This capacitor is known as a VARIABLE CAPACITOR, and is used whenever the capacitance in a circuit must frequently be changed. The station selector in a radio receiver is a typical example of a variable capacitor. A variable capacitor is illustrated in Figure 3-16.

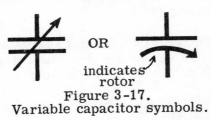

OR

indicates rotor

Figure 3-17.
Variable capacitor symbols.

Most variable capacitors are of the air dielectric type. A single variable capacitor consists of two sets of metal plates, insulated from each other and so arranged that one set of plates can be moved in relation to the other set. The stationary plates are the stator; the movable plates, the rotor. As the rotor is turned so that its plates mesh with the stator plates, the capacity increases. Figure 3-18 illustrates the rotor position of a variable

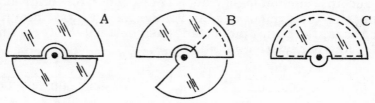

A. Minimum   B. Intermediate   C. Maximum
Figure 3-18. Variable capacitor settings.

capacitor for minimum, intermediate and maximum capacity. If several variable capacitors are connected on a common shaft so that all may be controlled at the same time, the result is known as a ganged capacitor. Figure 12-3 (in Chapter 12) illustrates a three-gang capacitor.

VOLTAGE RATING
    Capacitors are rated, not only in capacity, but also for the maximum voltage they will stand before breaking down. If the voltage across a capacitor is too high, the electrical pressure will force electrons to jump from the negative plate to the positive plate. This will puncture the dielectric and, in most cases, will ruin the capacitor.
    A typical capacitor would be rated as follows:
        Capacity - 8 ufd.
        DC working voltage - 450 V.
    "DC working voltage" indicates that the capacitor may be used in any circuit as long as the DC voltage or the AC peak voltage across it does not exceed 450 V.

CAPACITORS CONNECTED IN SERIES COMBINATION
    When two or more capacitors are connected end to end, as shown in Figures 3-19 and 3-20, the capacitors are said to be connected in series.

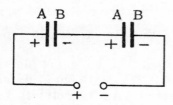

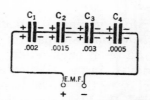

Figure 3-19. Capacitors in series.   Figure 3-20. Problem.

THE EFFECT OF CONNECTING CAPACITORS IN SERIES IS TO DECREASE THE TOTAL CAPACITANCE OF THE CIRCUIT, just as the total resistance of a circuit is decreased when resistors are connected in parallel.

The total capacity of capacitors connected in series can be computed by using the following formula:

$$(3\text{-}5) \quad C_T = \frac{1}{\dfrac{1}{C_1} + \dfrac{1}{C_2} + \dfrac{1}{C_3} + \text{etc.}}$$

PROBLEM: If four capacitors with capacities (in µfd.) shown in Figure 3-20 are connected in series, what is the total capacitance?

SOLUTION: Substitute in formula 3-5 the capacity values of the four capacitors shown in Figure 3-20.

$$(1) \quad C_T = \frac{1}{\dfrac{1}{.002} + \dfrac{1}{.0015} + \dfrac{1}{.003} + \dfrac{1}{.0005}}$$

Dividing .002 into 1, we get 500, etc.

$$(2) \quad C_T = \frac{1}{500 + 667 + 333 + 2000}$$

$$(3) \quad C_T = \frac{1}{3500} = .00029 \text{ ufd.}$$

From the above example, it should be clear that in a series arrangement of capacitors, the total capacity of the series combination (bank) is always less than the capacity of any individual capacitor in the bank.

CAPACITORS CONNECTED IN PARALLEL COMBINATION

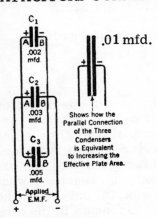

Figure 3-21.

Figure 3-21 illustrates three capacitors hooked together in parallel. Connecting capacitors in parallel has the effect of greatly increasing the effective plate area. Since the effective plate area is increased, the effective capacitance is also increased, as shown in Fig. 3-21.

When capacitors are connected in parallel, the resulting capacitance is equal to the sum of the individual capacitances. The total capacitance can be computed by using the following formula:

$$(3\text{-}6) \quad C_T = C_1 + C_2 + C_3, \text{ etc.}$$

PROBLEM: If three capacitors of .002

μfd., .003 μfd. and .005 μfd. are connected in parallel, what is the total capacitance?

SOLUTION: Use formula 3-6.

(1) $C_T = C_1 + C_2 + C_3$

(2) $C_T = .002 + .003 + .005 = .01$ μfd.

THE CAPACITOR IN AN ALTERNATING CURRENT CIRCUIT

If a capacitor is placed across an AC generator in series with an AC ammeter (as shown in Figure 3-22A), the following action occurs: When the left side of the generator is negative, electrons flow from the negative terminal of the generator to capacitor plate A. At the same time, electrons flow off plate B and through the ammeter to the right side of the generator. When the polarity of the AC generator reverses, as in Figure 3-22B, the electrons reverse in direction and flow from the left plate, through the generator and ammeter, onto the right plate. This reversal of current flow occurs many times in one second, depending upon the frequency of the generator. The ammeter registers a reversal of

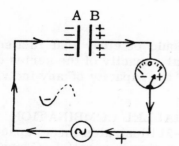 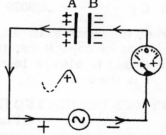

A. Negative Alternation   B. Positive Alternation.

Figure 3-22. Capacitor across AC generator.

current flow, since electrons flow through it, first in one direction and then in the other. In other words, although an electric current does not flow through the capacitor itself, it does flow in and out of the plates of the capacitor and therefore, flows back and forth through all the components connected in series with the capacitor. When it is said that AC flows through a capacitor, what is actually meant is that the current is flowing in and out of the plates of the capacitor. As far as the other components in the circuit are concerned, the AC might just as well be flowing through the capacitor.

CAPACITIVE REACTANCE

Figure 3-22A shows a capacitor connected across an AC generator. At the instant shown, (left side of generator is negative, right side is positive), electrons rush from the left side of the generator to the left plate of the capacitor. At first, only a few electrons will have reached the capacitor plate A. However, these few electrons will attempt to repel the electrons that are approaching this capacitor plate. This same action occurs on plate B when the polarity of the generator reverses itself. (See Figure 3-22B). The first few electrons to reach the right plate of the capacitor will oppose the electrons that are approaching this plate. Every time the polarity of the generator reverses, the first few electrons that pile up on the capacitor will repel the remaining electrons. Thus we see that a capacitor offers a certain amount of opposition to alternating current. This opposition is actually a COUNTER-EMF., since the original charge on the capacitor plates represents an opposition voltage to the generator voltage. This counter-emf. will vary inversely with the capacitance of the capacitor and the frequency of the AC generator. The higher the frequency of the generator, the less time there will be for electrons to charge the capacitor. The capacitor counter-emf., therefore, decreases with increase in generator frequency. As the capacitance of the capacitor increases, the charge will be distributed over an effectively larger plate area, decreasing the counter-emf. The counter-emf., therefore, decreases with an increase in capacitor capacitance.

The opposition or resistance that the capacitor offers to AC is called CAPACITIVE REACTANCE. The symbol for capacitive reactance is X_C and its unit is the OHM.

In order to compute the capacitive reactance of a capacitor in an AC circuit, the following formulas are used:

(1) When the capacity is given in farads:

(3-7) $X_C = \dfrac{1}{2 \pi fC}$

where: X_C = capacitive reactance in ohms, $2\pi = 6.28$,
f = frequency of AC in cycles, c = capacitance in farads.

(2) When the capacitance is given in microfarads:

(3-8) $X_C = \dfrac{1,000,000}{2 \pi fc}$

where: X_C = capacitive reactance in ohms, $2\pi = 6.28$,
f = frequency of AC in cycles, c = capacitance in microfarads
PROBLEM: Find the capacitive reactance of a 15 μfd capacitor in

an AC circuit where the frequency of the generator is 1 kilocycle.

SOLUTION: Use formula 3-8.

(1) $X_c = \dfrac{1,000,000}{2\pi fc}$ (2) $X_c = \dfrac{1,000,000}{6.28 \times 1000 \times 15}$

(3) $X_c = \dfrac{1,000,000}{94,200} = 10.6$ ohms.

In an AC circuit, a capacitor acts somewhat differently than a coil. The inductance of a coil OPPOSES CURRENT CHANGES by means of a self-induced emf.; a capacitor OPPOSES VOLTAGE CHANGES by means of the counter-emf. developed on its plates.

THE PHASE ANGLE

In an inductive circuit, we found that the current lags the impressed voltage. In a capacitive circuit, the opposite is true; THE CURRENT LEADS THE IMPRESSED VOLTAGE. This can be analyzed as follows: When a voltage or battery is first placed across a capacitor, there cannot be any back emf. across the capacitor because its plates are initially uncharged. A capacitor can only have a voltage across its plates provided there is a charge on its plates. If the charge is initially zero, then the counter voltage must be initially zero. Since the capacitor offers no initial back emf., the initial current in to it is at maximum. Therefore, the current is at a maximum when the voltage is still zero; or, the current leads the voltage. When the current falls to zero, the voltage just reaches its maximum value.

The current leads the source voltage by 90° in a pure capacitive circuit. (See Figure 3-23). If we introduce some resistance into the circuit, the current will lead the voltage by less than 90°. When the resistance and capacitive reactance are equal, the current will lead the voltage by 45°. The greater the resistance in the circuit, the smaller is the phase angle.

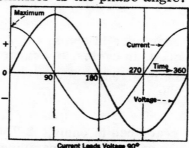

Figure 3-23.   Pure capacitive circuit.

IMPEDANCE OF SERIES CIRCUITS

In a previous paragraph, we discussed the impedance of a series circuit containing resistance and inductive reactance. We learned that the total impedance of the circuit was not the simple sum of the resistance and the inductive reactance. The same is true for the impedance of a circuit containing resistance and capacitive reactance. The formula that is used to determine the impedance of an inductive circuit is: $Z = \sqrt{R^2 + X_L{}^2}$.

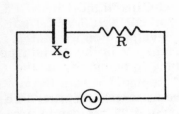

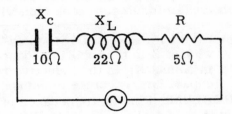

Figure 3-24. R-C circuit.   Figure 3-25. R-L-C circuit.

To determine the impedance of a capacitive circuit, we use the same formula, except that we substitute X_c for X_L. The formula now becomes:

(3-9) $Z = \sqrt{R^2 + X_c{}^2}$ ohms   where: R = series resistance in ohms
X_c = capacitive reactance in ohms

PROBLEM: If, in a resistive-capacitive circuit, $X_c = 4$ ohms and R = 3 ohms, what is the total impedance?

SOLUTION: Use formula 3-9.

(1) $Z = \sqrt{R^2 + X_c{}^2}$ (2) $Z = \sqrt{3^2 + 4^2}$

(3) $Z = \sqrt{9 + 16}$ (4) $Z = \sqrt{25} = 5$ ohms

IMPEDANCE OF SERIES R-L-C CIRCUITS

Observe the series circuit of Figure 3-25. Notice that this circuit contains resistance, inductance and capacitance. What is the relationship of X_L to X_c, and how can we figure out the impedance of such a circuit? The effects of X_L and X_c on the current in a series AC circuit can be understood by considering the game "Tug-of-war". The rope represents the current and the men pulling on the rope in opposite directions represent the actions of X_L and X_c on the current. X_L and X_c act on the current in opposition. If X_L and X_c are equal, they will have no effect on the current since their effects will cancel. If X_L is larger than X_c, it will be the difference between X_L and X_C which will affect the current. Conversely, if X_C is larger than X_L, it will also be the difference between X_C and X_L which will affect the current. Before we can determine the impedance of the circuit, we must calculate the total reactance. The total reactance of the circuit is the difference between the two reactances, X_L and X_C. This difference is then added to the resistance in a manner similar to that of formula 3-9.

The following formula is used to find the impedance of a circuit containing Resistance, Inductance and Capacitance:

$$(3\text{-}10) \quad Z = \sqrt{R^2 + (X_L - X_C)^2}$$

where: Z is the total impedance in ohms, R is the resistance in ohms, X_L is the inductive reactance in ohms, X_C is the capacitive reactance in ohms.

PROBLEM: Find the impedance of a circuit which contains a resistance of 5 ohms, an inductive reactance of 22 ohms and a capacitive reactance of 10 ohms. (See Figure 3-25).

SOLUTION: Use formula 3-10.

$$(1) \quad Z = \sqrt{R^2 + (X_L - X_C)^2}$$

$$(2) \quad Z = \sqrt{R^2 + (22 - 10)^2} = \sqrt{25 + (12)^2}$$

$$(3) \quad Z = \sqrt{25 + 144} = \sqrt{169} = 13 \text{ ohms}$$

SERIES RESONANCE

In the previous paragraph, we studied a series AC circuit containing resistance, inductance and capacitance. In order to find the impedance of such a circuit, we had to use formula 3-10.

Let us assume that the values of L, C and the frequency of the AC generator are so chosen that X_L and X_C are equal. In this case, the quantity $(X_L - X_C)$ in formula 3-10 would be equal to zero. The two reactances are equal and cancel each other. (Recall the analogy of the game of tug-of-war.) The only opposition that remains in the circuit is the resistance, R. Therefore, the IMPEDANCE IN A CIRCUIT, CONTAINING EQUAL AMOUNTS OF INDUCTIVE AND CAPACITIVE REACTANCE, IS EQUAL TO THE RESISTANCE IN THE CIRCUIT. The current flowing in the circuit is at its maximum value; the impedance of the circuit is at its minimum value. The condition where the inductive reactance is equal to the capacitive reactance in a circuit is known as RESONANCE. Since the components of this circuit are in series, the circuit is known as a SERIES RESONANT CIRCUIT. The frequency of the generator at resonance is called the RESONANT FRE-QUENCY.

If the frequency of the AC generator is increased, the induc-tive reactance will go up and the capacitive reactance will go down. The difference between the reactances is a number larger than zero. Our circuit is, therefore, no longer resonant. The imped-ance of the circuit has increased since the resistance is no longer the sole opposition to current flow. The impedance of the circuit is now determined by formula 3-10. Since the circuit impedance has increased, the current will now decrease below its resonance value.

THE RESONANCE CURVE

If we were to draw a curve of the variations of current with changes in generator frequency, we would obtain a curve known as a RESONANCE CURVE. This is illus-trated in Figure 3-26. The vertical di-rection represents the amount of cur-rent flowing in the circuit for different frequencies. The horizontal direction represents the different generator fre-quencies. As the frequency of the gen-erator is varied above and below the resonant frequency, the current will vary in the manner indicated. Notice that the current reaches a peak only at resonance and decreases in value at either side of resonance.

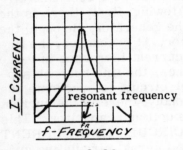

Figure 3-26.
The resonance curve.

RESONANT FREQUENCY OF A SERIES CIRCUIT

For every value of inductance and capacitance in a series cir-cuit, there is ONE frequency at which the inductive reactance equals the capacitive reactance. This frequency is referred to as the resonant frequency. The resonant frequency can be calculated by using the following formula:

$$(3\text{-}11) \quad f_R = \frac{1}{2\pi\sqrt{LC}}$$

where: f_R is the resonant frequency in cycles, 2π is 6.28,

L is the inductance in henries, C is the capacitance in farads

In order to find the resonant frequency, when L and C are given in more common units such as microhenries and microfar-ads, the above formula is modified as follows:

$$(3-11A) \quad f_R = \frac{1,000,000}{2\pi\sqrt{LC}}$$

where: f_R is the resonant frequency in cycles, 2π is 6.28, L is the inductance in microhenries and C is the capacitance in microfarads.

It is important to remember that the resonant frequency of a circuit goes up when either the inductance or capacitance goes down. This becomes apparent if we inspect the above formula.

PARALLEL RESONANCE

Figure 3-27 illustrates a coil and capacitor connected in parallel across an AC generator. Note that R_L represents the DC resistance of the coil. If the frequency of the generator is adjusted so that X_L is equal to X_C, we would have a condition of resonance known as PARALLEL RESONANCE. In a parallel resonant circuit, there are two different currents flowing; first, there is the line current (I_{Line}) which flows from the generator, through the resonant circuit and back to the generator. At resonance, the line current is very low in value. The line current increases in value above and below resonance. At resonance, the line current supplies just enough energy to the parallel circuit to overcome the losses in the resistance of the coil. Secondly, there is the current which flows back and forth between the coil and capacitor. This current, I_C, is called the INTERNAL CIRCULATING CURRENT (or TANK CIRCUIT). At resonance, the internal circulating current is very high compared to the line current. Since the reactances of the coil and capacitor are equal and cancel each other, the only opposition to the internal circulating current at resonance is the resistance of the coil "R_L".

To understand the operation of the parallel resonant circuit

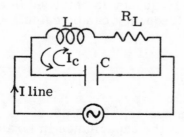

Figure 3-27.
Parallel resonance.

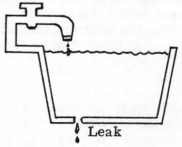

Figure 3-28. Water tank.

more clearly, we can compare it to a water tank with a small leak in its bottom. See Figure 3-28. The small leak represents the resistance of the coil. The tank represents the circuit of the coil and capacitor in parallel. (The parallel combination of a coil and capacitor is actually given the name TANK CIRCUIT). The water in the tank represents the energy present in the tank circuit due to the internal circulating current flowing between the coil and capacitor. The faucet represents the generator and the water flowing from the faucet into the tank represents the line current.

If there were no leak, the water tank would not lose any water and there would be no need to add water from the faucet. Similarly, if the electronic circuit had no resistance, no energy would be dissipated as the internal circulating current flows back and forth between the coil and capacitor. (Energy can only be dissipated in a resistance). Therefore, the generator would not have to supply any energy since none would be lost in the circuit. Consequently, the line current would be zero. Practically speaking, there will always be some resistance present in the tank circuit. Energy will necessarily be dissipated in the tank circuit since the internal circulating current must flow through the resistance of the coil. In order to replenish this lost energy, the generator will have to supply energy by way of the line current flowing into the tank circuit.

IMPEDANCE OF THE PARALLEL RESONANT CIRCUIT

The average tank circuit encountered in radio has a very low coil resistance. The energy dissipated will therefore be very low, and the line current will also be very low. Since the line current is small, the impedance (opposition to the line current) of a parallel resonant circuit must be very high. Compare this with the low impedance of a series resonant circuit. We will also find that the impedance of the parallel resonant circuit decreases as the frequency of the energy that is injected into the tank circuit varies above and below the resonant frequency.

SUMMARY OF CHARACTERISTICS OF SERIES AND PARALLEL RESONANT CIRCUITS

	Series Resonant Circuit	Parallel Resonant Circuit
Impedance	low	high
Current	high	line current - low. Internal circulating current - high.
E across circuit	low	high

AC POWER

In a previous paragraph, we learned that the power loss in a DC circuit is determined by using the following formulas:

$$(1)\ P = EI \qquad (2)\ P = I^2R \qquad (3)\ P = \frac{E^2}{R}$$

where: R is the total resistance in the circuit.

This power is dissipated in the form of heat and is considered to be wasted energy.

The power loss in a pure resistive AC circuit is similarly determined, using the same formulas where E and I are in effective values.

$$(3\text{-}12)\ (1)\ P = E_{eff}. \times I_{eff}.$$
$$(2)\ P = I^2_{eff}. \times R \qquad (3)\ P = \frac{E^2_{eff}.}{R}$$

where: P is the power in watts.

In an AC circuit containing either inductance or capacitance, the voltage and current are out of phase. (They are not acting together at the same instant). Therefore, the above formulas cannot be used to determine the TRUE POWER loss in a reactive circuit. The product of E_{eff}. and I_{eff}. would, in this case, be known as the APPARENT POWER loss. This power is actually larger than the true power consumed in the circuit. The true power is the heat dissipated in the circuit. The electric company charges you for the true power consumed over a period of time. Power can only be dissipated or used up in a resistive element. Power cannot be dissipated in a pure capacitive or pure inductive circuit.

The apparent power can be determined from the readings of a voltmeter and ammeter placed in the circuit, as illustrated in Figure 3-29. The product of these readings, volts times amperes or VOLT-AMPERES, is the apparent power. The true power dissipated will always be indicated by an instrument called a WATT-METER.

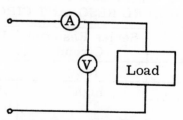

Figure 3-29. Determining apparent power.

The one formula which can be used to determine the true power consumed in both DC and AC circuits is:

$$P = I^2R$$

where: I is either the DC current or the effective AC current and R is the resistance in the circuit.

THE TRANSFORMER

The voltage supplied to most communities in the United States is the standard 117 volts AC. Practically all television sets and most radios require a voltage higher than 117 volts in order to operate satisfactorily. To fill this need, a device is incorporated in these sets to step-up the line voltage from 117 volts to a higher voltage. The device which can increase or decrease the value of an AC voltage is called a TRANSFORMER.

PRINCIPLE OF THE TRANSFORMER

You will recall from our earlier discussion of AC voltage, that an emf. will be induced in a loop of wire which cuts a magnetic field. As long as there is relative motion between the loop and the magnetic field, a voltage will be generated. If the loop is kept stationary and the magnetic field cuts across the loop of wire, the result obtained will be the same as if the loop were in motion instead of the magnetic field. In either case, a voltage will be induced in the conductors of the loop. The transformer operation is based upon a varying magnetic field inducing a voltage in a stationary coil of wire.

OPERATION OF THE TRANSFORMER

Every time current flows through a conductor, a magnetic field builds up around the conductor. The magnetic field is in phase with the current at all times. Therefore, if an alternating current flows through a coil of wire, an alternating magnetic field expands outwardly away from the coil and collapses back into the

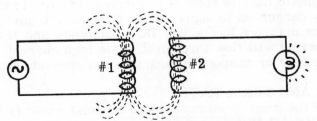

Figure 3-30. Magnetic coupling.

coil periodically. If a second coil with a lamp across it is placed in the vicinity of coil #1, as illustrated in Figure 3-30, the alternating magnetic field will cut across coil #2 and induce an AC voltage in it; This voltage will cause the lamp to light. Notice that no electrical connection exists between the coils. Energy is transferred from coil #1 to coil #2 by means of the varying magnetic field. We say that the coils are MAGNETICALLY COUPLED. The entire device consisting of two coils magnetically coupled, is known as a TRANSFORMER. Coil #1 which is connected to the voltage source is called the PRIMARY. Coil #2, in which the induced voltage is developed, is called the SECONDARY.

THE POWER TRANSFORMER

The transformer in Figure 3-31B is known as an air-core transformer. Its use is confined to radio frequencies and it will be considered later on. A transformer which is used to transfer AC power at power frequencies is known as a POWER TRANSFORMER.

In order for a power transformer to operate efficiently, the primary and secondary are wound on an iron core, as illustrated in Figure 3-31A.

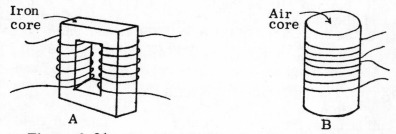

Iron
core

Air
core

A   B

Figure 3-31. Iron-core and Air-core transformers.

Power transformers can only be used on AC because an alternating magnetic field is required to induce an emf. in the secondary. It is dangerous to apply DC to the power transformer primary. The primary has a low DC resistance and therefore, a high DC current will flow through it. This high current will either blow a line fuse or damage the transformer beyond repair.

VOLTAGE AND TURNS RATIO

One of the most common uses of a transformer is to step-up the 117 volts AC that is supplied to the average home. All AC radios and television sets require several hundred volts to operate.

Therefore, they must incorporate a transformer which will step-up the 117 volts. A fundamental principle of transformer action states that the voltage ratio between the secondary and the primary varies directly as the turns ratio. An example will clarify this point. If there are three times as many turns on the secondary as on the primary, the voltage of the secondary will be three times the voltage that is applied to the primary. Figure 3-32 illustrates this principle. Notice that the transformer secondary has three

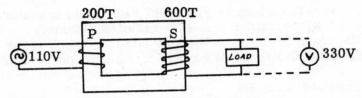

Figure 3-32. 1 to 3 step-up transformer.

times as many turns as its primary. If the primary voltage is 110 volts, the secondary voltage which appears across the load will be 330 volts. If there are ten times as many turns on the secondary as on the primary, the secondary voltage will be ten times as great as the primary voltage. A transformer whose secondary voltage is greater than the primary voltage, is known as a STEP-UP TRANSFORMER.

Figure 3-33 shows a transformer where the turns on the secondary are less than the turns on the primary. In this case, the voltage will be stepped down from the primary to the secondary. This transformer is known as a STEP-DOWN TRANSFORMER. If 100 volts were applied to the primary winding, the secondary voltage would be 50 volts.

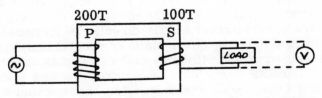

Figure 3-33. 2 to 1 step-down transformer.

TRANSFORMER SYMBOLS

Figure 3-34 shows the schematic symbols of typical transformers used in radio circuits.

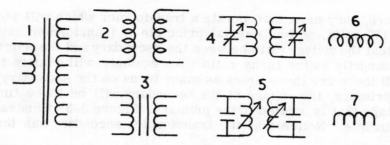

Figure 34. Transformer symbols. #1 - power transformer. #2 - RF transformer. #3 - audio transformer. #4 &
#5 - IF transformers. Note that either symbol #6 or #7
may be used to represent coils of a transformer or choke.

TRANSFORMER LOSSES

There are three types of losses which are encountered in the
operation of a transformer. They are:
(1) EDDY CURRENTS
(2) HYSTERESIS LOSSES
(3) COPPER LOSSES

EDDY CURRENTS are wasted currents induced in the iron
core of the transformer by the varying magnetic field. These currents take a circular path through the core material, as shown in
Figure 3-35A. Since the resistance in the path of the eddy currents in a solid core material is low, the eddy currents will be
large. Eddy currents serve only to heat up the iron core and,
therefore, represent a power loss. Eddy current losses can be
reduced by having the core made up of LAMINATIONS (thin insulated iron sheets) instead of solid iron. See Figure 3-35B. The
laminations limit the eddy currents by increasing the resistance
in their path of flow.

HYSTERESIS LOSSES represent the energy that is used up in
forcing the iron core to reverse the direction of its magnetic field
every time the current reverses its direction. Hysteresis losses
can be minimized by using cores made of special materials. Hysteresis losses, together with eddy current losses, are known as
IRON-CORE LOSSES.

The third type of loss encountered in transformers is called
COPPER LOSSES. Copper losses are caused by the resistance
of the wire which makes up the turns of the windings. Current
flowing through the resistance of the winding develops an I^2R power loss in the form of wasteful heat. Copper losses can be minimized by using a heavier wire for the windings; a thicker wire
will have a lower resistance and therefore, a lower I^2R loss.

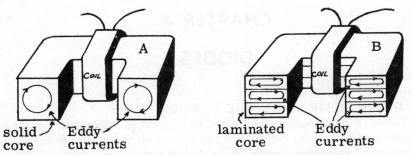

Figure 3-35A. High Eddy-current flow in solid core.
Figure 3-35B. Low Eddy-current flow in laminated core.

MAXIMUM POWER TRANSFER

In order that there is a maximum transfer of energy from a generator to a load, the impedance of the load should equal the internal impedance of the generator. This law applies to all circuits in radio and electricity.

Sometimes a load, such as a speaker, may have a very low impedance compared to the very high internal impedance of the vacuum tube which is to energize the speaker. In order that there be maximum energy transfer between the vacuum tube (generator) and the speaker (load), a matching transformer (output transformer) is interposed between the two. The transformer steps up the impedance. We say that the transformer MATCHES the load to the generator, thus effecting maximum power transfer. Impedance matching is an important function of a transformer.

CHAPTER 4

DIODES

THE DEVELOPMENT OF THE VACUUM TUBE

Thomas A. Edison was one of the great pioneers in the development of the vacuum tube. Edison invented the incandescent light bulb whose basic principles were later put to use by men such as Fleming and DeForest, in the development of the modern vacuum tube.

Edison's incandescent electric lamp, which was the forerunner of the modern electric bulb, consisted of a resistance wire called a filament, enclosed within a glass envelope. The air within the glass envelope had been removed to create a vacuum. The ends of the resistance wire protruded through the glass, as illustrated in Figure 4-1. If a current was passed through the resistance wire, it heated up and glowed. We can then say that the filament was heated to INCANDESCENCE.

While working with his electric light, Edison discovered that the incandescent wire emitted, or boiled off, electrons. These electrons remained around the wire in the form of an electron cloud or SPACE CHARGE. This phenomenon of electron emission is known as the EDISON EFFECT and is the basis of the operation of all vacuum tubes.

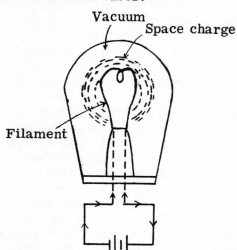

Figure 4-1. The electric lamp.

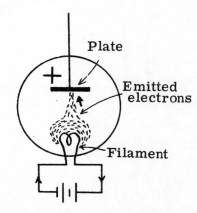

Figure 4-2. Positive plate attracting electrons.

ELECTRON EMISSION

Many metallic substances will emit electrons when heated to incandescence. For instance, the resistance wire in the light bulb emits electrons. These emitted electrons are wasted since they serve no useful purpose.

The vacuum tube is similar to the light bulb in that it also contains a resistance wire which emits electrons when heated. The vacuum tube, however, is designed to make use of the emitted electrons. In addition to the resistance wire, the vacuum tube has a positively charged collector of electrons called the PLATE. The plate is also known as an ANODE. The positive plate attracts the emitted electrons. This is illustrated in Figure 4-2. The purpose of the battery in Figure 4-2 is to force current through the filament, thereby heating it.

THE CATHODE

The element in the vacuum tube which supplies the electrons for the tube's operation is known as the CATHODE. The cathode emits or boils off electrons when energy in the form of heat is supplied to it. There are two different types of cathodes used in vacuum tubes. They are the directly-heated and the indirectly-heated types. We will now discuss these two types in detail.

(1) The directly-heated cathode. This type is also known by the name FILAMENT-CATHODE. An example of a filament-cathode is illustrated in Figure 4-3. The heating current is passed directly through the cathode wire, which is made of tungsten. The current heats up the cathode wire, which then emits electrons from its surface. Directly heated filament-cathodes usually require very little heating power. Therefore, they are used in tubes designed for portable battery operation because it is necessary to impose as small a drain as possible on the batteries. Examples of battery-operated filament-cathode tubes are the 1A7, the 1R5 and the 1U4.

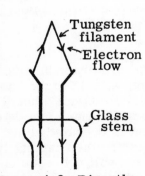

Figure 4-3. Directly heated cathode.

(2) The indirectly-heated cathode. This type is also known as the HEATER-CATHODE and is illustrated in Figure 4-4A. The heater-cathode consists of the following two parts: (1) A thin metal sleeve or cylinder coated with electron-emitting material; this sleeve is the cathode; and (2) A heater wire which is insulated

from the sleeve. The heater is usually made of a tungsten material. Current flows through the filament and heats it up. The
cathode, being close to the filament, also heats up. Since the cathode has an electron emitting surface, the heat will cause it to emit
electrons. Note that the heater function, in this case, is not to
emit electrons, but merely to heat the cathode. The heater wire
is known as the filament. Figure 4-4B shows the schematic symbol for the heater-cathode.

Almost all present day receiving tubes designed for AC operation are of the indirectly-heated cathode type.

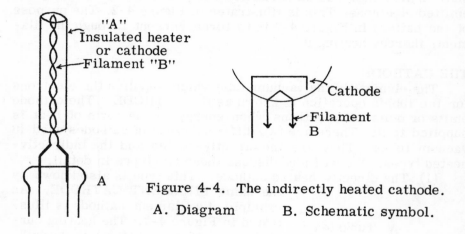

Figure 4-4. The indirectly heated cathode.

A. Diagram   B. Schematic symbol.

FILAMENT OPERATING VOLTAGE

The first number in a tube designation usually indicates the
proper filament operating voltage. For example, a 6X4 tube should
have its filament operated at 6.3 volts. All filaments should be
operated at their designated operating voltages, which are determined by the manufacturers. If the filament is operated above its
rated voltage, the excessive current will shorten the filament life.
Operating the filament below its rated voltage will decrease electron emission and lower the tube operating efficiency. The proper
filament voltage for a particular tube, as well as other tube characteristics, can be found in a tube manual.

THE DIODE

Let us see how electrons emitted from the cathode can be col-
lected and made to do useful work. Electrons are negatively
charged and will be attracted by a positively charged object. Therefore, if a positively charged object called a PLATE is put into the

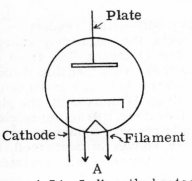

Figure 4-5A. Indirectly heated.

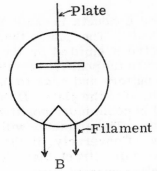

Figure 4-5B. Directly heated.

vacuum tube, it will serve as a collector of electrons. A vacuum tube which contains a plate and a cathode is known as a DIODE. The schematic symbol for a diode is shown in Figure 4-5. B is a directly-heated diode and A is an indirectly-heated diode.

The plate and the cathode are known as the ELEMENTS of the vacuum tube. The diode is, therefore, a two-element tube. The heater of the indirectly-heated tube is not counted as a separate element.

THE DIODE AS A CONDUCTOR

Figure 4-6 illustrates a simplified schematic of a diode with the plate connected to the positive terminal of a battery; the cathode is connected through a switch to the negative terminal. The instant the switch is closed, the ammeter in the circuit will register a current flow, indicating that electrons are flowing from the cathode to the plate. The diode is said to be CONDUCTING. The

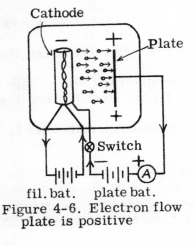

Figure 4-6. Electron flow plate is positive

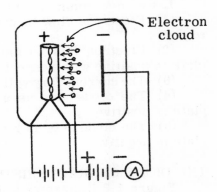

Figure 4-7. Diode action when plate is negative.

diode conducts because the plate is positive with respect to the cathode. The plate, therefore, attracts the negatively charged electrons emitted by the cathode. The electrons flow from the plate to the positive terminal of the battery. They then flow through the battery and back to the cathode, where they once more can be emitted to the plate. If the battery voltage is increased, the plate will become more positive and will, therefore, attract more electrons. The ammeter will consequently register a larger current flow. Conversely, if the plate battery voltage is decreased, the plate will attract less electrons and the ammeter will register a smaller current flow.

When the diode conducts, it represents a very low resistance path between the cathode and plate. For all practical purposes, we can consider a conducting diode as a closed switch between the cathode and plate.

THE DIODE AS A NON-CONDUCTOR

If we reverse the battery connections, as shown in Figure 4-7, the plate becomes negative and the cathode positive. Since the negative plate will not attract electrons, the diode will NOT CONDUCT. The diode, therefore, acts like an open switch and permits no current to flow. The ammeter will consequently read zero amperes. The emitted negatively-charged electrons are repelled by the negative plate and remain close to the cathode where they form an ELECTRON CLOUD. The cloud of electrons around the cathode is known as a SPACE CHARGE. If the plate were to become positive once again, the space charge would be rapidly reduced since its electrons would be attracted to the plate. The cathode is free once again to emit electrons.

Let us now summarize the operation of the diode:

(1) Electrons flow in one direction only - from the cathode to plate.

(2) Electron flow to the plate will take place only when the plate is positive with respect to the cathode.

(3) The current flow will vary with the plate to cathode voltage.

(4) The diode acts as a conductor (short circuit) when the plate is positive.

(5) The diode acts as a non-conductor (open circuit) when the plate is negative.

THE DIODE CHARACTERISTIC CURVE

Figure 4-8 illustrates a diode connected to a source of variable voltage. The heater circuit has been omitted for the purpose of simplicity. "A" is a milliammeter connected in series with

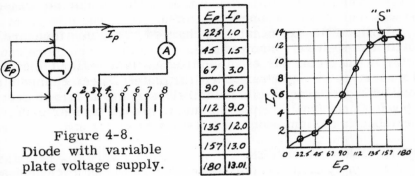

E_p	I_p
22.5	1.0
45	1.5
67	3.0
90	6.0
112	9.0
135	12.0
157	13.0
180	13.01

Figure 4-8.
Diode with variable
plate voltage supply.

Figure 4-9. Plot of plate current
against plate voltage.

the tube. The voltage applied to the plate of the diode can be varied by changing the position of the plate tap from position #1 to position #8. As the tap is moved from position #1 to position #8, the plate to cathode voltage increases. For every value of plate voltage, there will be a different value of diode plate current, as measured by the milliammeter. The table in Figure 4-9 is a tabulation of plate current readings for various values of plate voltage. If we plot these readings on the graph in Figure 4-9 and then draw a line through the different points, we obtain a curve known as the DIODE CHARACTERISTIC CURVE. I_p is the electronic symbol for plate current; E_p is the electronic symbol for plate to cathode voltage, or simply plate voltage. The plate current-plate voltage curve shows the amount of current that a particular diode will conduct for a given plate voltage. The curve indicates that as the plate voltage increases, the plate current also increases up to the point "S". Beyond point "S", the curve becomes practically horizontal. In other words, as the plate voltage increases beyond point "S", the plate current remains essentially constant and will not increase, regardless of plate voltage increases. The point "S" is known as the saturation point. It is the point at which the plate is collecting all of the electrons that the cathode is capable of emitting.

The characteristic curve is important because it tells us at a glance what the plate current will be for any particular plate voltage. This information is useful if we are designing a diode circuit for a certain application. Characteristic curves for diodes, as well as all other tubes, are found in tube manuals.

SUMMARY OF FILAMENTS AND DIODE TUBES

(1) The emission of electrons from a filament is the principle upon which all electron tubes are based.

(2) Electrons are negatively charged particles which are attracted to a positively charged plate.

(3) A diode consists of an emitting surface called the cathode and a receiver of electrons called the plate. These elements are placed within an evacuated (vacuum) glass or metal bulb to prevent the hot filament from burning up, and to provide a clear path from the cathode to the plate for the fast-moving electrons.

SEMICONDUCTOR DIODES

In the early days of radio, a receiver known as a "crystal set" was very popular. The original crystal sets used earphones because the amplifier tubes that were required to operate a speaker were quite expensive.

When tubes became less costly and demand for speaker-operated receivers became strong, the crystal set began to disappear. However, the "crystal" itself, in a somewhat different form, has made a strong comeback. Today, it is known as a solid-state semiconductor.

The diode semiconductor is used in just about every radio and television set. Its popularity is based on the fact that, unlike the tube, it does not require a socket; it is light in weight and can be soldered directly into a circuit. Furthermore, it has no filament and so its operation is instantaneous. The semiconductor diode works both as a rectifier and a detector. Let us see how this type of diode functions, why it works and also, how it differs from a vacuum tube.

INSULATORS

Certain substances and certain elements are good conductors; others are good insulators. Copper wire is a good conductor, while glass is a good insulator. The element iron is put in the conductor class, while other elements, such as pure germanium, selenium or pure silicon, are insulators.

We can modify the characteristics of any element by mixing in other elements. For example, we can add elements such as boron, antimony or arsenic to pure germanium or pure silicon and thus, change these elements from non-conductors into conductors.

DOPING

The addition of an element, such as antimony, to either germanium or silicon, is known as doping. Since the germanium or silicon, at the start, is as pure as it can be made, the added element is referred to as an impurity. It takes just a very small amount of impurity to modify the germanium or silicon so that they are no longer insulators.

All elements are made up of atoms and each atom contains a nucleus surrounded by one or more rings of electrons. By diffusing certain elements, such as antimony, into pure germanium or silicon, we change the total number of electrons in the germanium or silicon. These "doped" elements now have more electrons than they originally had. Since electrons are negatively charged, we refer to them as negative germanium or negative silicon. We abbreviate negative germanium as n-germanium or n-type germanium. The antimony, diffused into the pure germanium or silicon is referred to as a "donor" element since it has, in effect, donated or contributed electrons.

We can diffuse other substances into germanium or silicon - substances that have a deficiency of electrons. An element, such as boron, for example, likes to borrow electrons and so, when mixed with germanium or silicon, will take electrons from these substances. For this reason, we call boron an acceptor element - it accepts or takes away electrons.

When a substance or an element loses electrons, it is no longer neutral. It has become less negative or, stated in another way, has become more positive. We can also refer to an atom that has lost an electron as a "hole". The "hole" is the positive charge around the atom due to the removal of one of its electrons by the acceptor. Germanium or silicon, doped with boron, are referred to as positive germanium or positive silicon. We abbreviate this as p-germanium or p-silicon or p-type. We can represent n-type or p-type pictorially, as shown in Figure 4-10. The minus signs indicate an excess of negative charges; the plus signs tell us that we have a shortage of electrons or an excess of positive "holes".

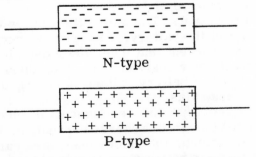

N-type

P-type

Figure 4-10. N-type and P-type germanium or silicon.

THE SEMICONDUCTOR DIODE

If we take a block of p-type germanium and a block of n-type germanium (or silicon) and put them together, we will have a semiconductor diode. The semiconductor diode is referred to as a solid-state device.

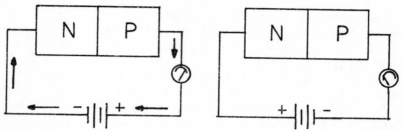

Fig. 4-11A. Forward biasing.　Fig. 4-11B. Reverse biasing.

In Figure 4-11, we have a battery connected across our two blocks of doped germanium or silicon. In drawing A, the negative terminal of the battery is connected to the n-type material, while the positive terminal is connected to the p-type material. Connecting a voltage in this manner is known as biasing. Electrons will now flow from the battery, through the n-type material, into the p-type material and back to the battery. The reason for the current flow is that the battery urges or forces electrons into the n-type block, which already has more electrons than normal. The electrons migrate over to the p-type block since this region is more positive and attracts them. However, as electrons leave the p-type block to the battery, more electrons from the n-type block cross the junction between the two blocks, and so the process is a continuous one. The current that flows is referred to as a forward current. The voltage producing this current is then called a forward voltage or forward bias.

Now examine drawing B. The only difference is that we have reversed the polarity of the battery. As a result, very little current flows. The small current that does flow moves in an opposite direction to the way it previously moved. We, therefore, call it a reverse current and the battery voltage is referred to as a reverse voltage or reverse bias.

Aside from the fact that the semiconductor diode in Figure 4-11 does have a small amount of reverse current, its basic action is very much like the vacuum tube diode described earlier in this chapter. Note that there is no filament or cathode to be heated and

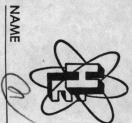

HONOLULU ELECTRONICS

A Division of Kaimuki Radio Co., Ltd.

Phone 949-5564

819 Keeaumoku Street

Wholesale Electronic Distributors

Honolulu, Hawaii 96814

INVOICE NO.

77141

NAME

ADDRESS

DATE 10/16/76

CUST ORDER NO.	
CALL NO.	
REQ'N. NO.	
CUSTOMER'S PHONE	

DELIVERY INSTRUCTIONS:

SALESMAN	CASH	CHARGE	C.O.D.	WHOLESALE	FED. GOV'T	PARTIAL	COMPLETE
☐	☐	☐	☐	☐	☐	☐	☐

Quantity	Description	List	Net	Amount
1	tweed 3-01			1 25
				28
				2 03

PRINTED BY THE STANDARD REGISTER COMPANY, U.S.A. ZIPSET ®

ACKNO

OD CONDITION

ATURE

TERMS: 30 DAYS NET.

so, unlike the tube, the semiconductor diode does not get warm or hot when operating. Therefore, since we do not need to wait for the filament or cathode to get hot enough to emit electrons, the semiconductor diode acts at once.

CHAPTER 5

POWER SUPPLIES

RECTIFICATION

Vacuum tubes in receivers and transmitters will only operate when connected to a direct current source of power. Portable radios, for example, are energized by batteries which are, in themselves, a source of direct current. As noted previously, the electrical power that is delivered to most homes throughout the country today is alternating current. If we were to connect the tubes in our radios directly to the AC wall outlet, the radio would not operate because a radio tube needs a source of DC power. We all know that our radios do operate when we plug them into the AC socket. Obviously, there must be something in the radio which converts the alternating current into direct current. The device in a radio which converts the alternating current into direct current is known as a RECTIFIER. The process of conversion is called RECTIFICATION.

THE DIODE AS A HALF-WAVE RECTIFIER

The ability of the diode vacuum tube or the semiconductor diode to pass current in only one direction makes it possible to convert alternating current into direct current. Let us see how this is done. Figure 5-1 illustrates a simple diode rectifier circuit. When terminal "B" of the AC generator is positive with respect to terminal "A", the diode plate becomes positive with respect to its cathode. The diode therefore conducts current in the direction indicated by the arrows. The DC milliammeter will deflect to the value of the current flow.

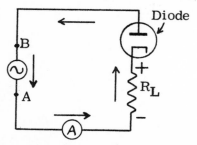

Figure 5-1. Diode used as half-wave rectifier.

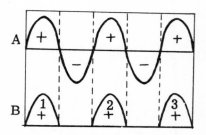

Figure 5-2. Half-wave rectifier wave-forms.

On the next half of the alternating current cycle, the polarity of the generator will be reversed, making the plate negative with respect to the cathode. The diode will stop conducting because a negative plate will repel the electron flow. The current in the cir- cuit will therefore cease flowing during the negative half of the cycle. When the polarity of the AC generator again reverses itself and makes the diode plate positive, current will again flow through the circuit. Figure 5-2 is a graphic explanation of what is happen- ing. Figure 5-2A shows the sine wave which is generated across the terminals of the AC generator. Figure 5-2B shows the wave which is obtained across the load resistor R_L. In Figure 5-2B, we see the positive halves of the cycle when the plate of the diode is positive with respect to the cathode. At that time, the diode conducts and acts as a short circuit. The positive half cycles are therefore impressed directly across the resistor R_L. During the negative half of each AC cycle, the tube does not conduct and is an open circuit. During these times, there is no voltage developed across the resistor since there is no current flow. The current through the resistor is therefore a pulsating direct current and the voltage across the resistor is a pulsating direct voltage. Even though the current flows in spurts or pulses through the resistor, the current is still DC because it flows in ONE direction only. This action of the diode in passing only one-half of the AC input wave to the load resistor is known as HALF-WAVE RECTIFICATION.

The ends of the load resistance have been marked with a po- larity because electrons are entering and emerging from this re- sistance. The end at which they enter becomes more negative than the end from which they emerge. The pulsating direct-voltage, if properly filtered, can be utilized to operate a radio receiver.

We can replace the AC generator of Figure 5-1 with a trans- former, as shown in Figure 5-3, without altering the operation of the circuit. The transformer merely steps up the AC voltage and the action is the same as in Figure 5-1.

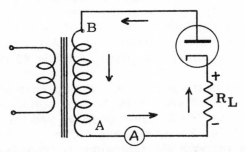

Figure 5-3. Diode used as half-wave rectifier.

THE DIODE AS A FULL-WAVE RECTIFIER

In half-wave rectification, only the positive half of the AC input is used. The negative alternations are completely cut off and wasted. If we could somehow utilize the negative as well as the positive alternation, we would be operating our rectifier system more efficiently. This is accomplished in full-wave rectification.

We can modify the half-wave rectifier circuit of Figure 5-3 by adding another diode and center-tapping the transformer secondary. The resulting circuit is illustrated in Figure 5-4. The cathodes of the diodes are connected together and the circuit is known as a FULL-WAVE RECTIFIER. The operation of a full-wave rectifier is as follows:

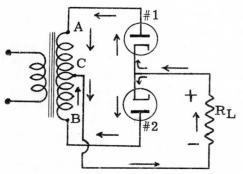

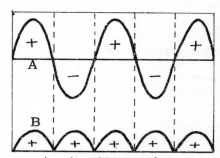

A. input wave-form.
B. output wave-form.

Figure 5-4. Full-wave rectifier.   Figure 5-5. Full-wave rectifier wave-forms.

When an AC voltage is impressed across the primary of the transformer, an AC voltage will be induced in the secondary. When point "A" is positive with respect to point "B", the plate of diode #1 is positive and the tube conducts. The electrons flow through the transformer, from A to C, out of C, into the load resistance R_L. From R_L, the electrons flow to the cathode of diode #1. Since the tube is conducting (because of its positive plate), the current flows to the plate and back to point A to complete its circuit. During all this time, the plate of diode #2 is negative and does not conduct.

On the next half of the AC cycle, the bottom of the transformer, point "B", goes positive, while the top, point "A", goes negative. The plate of diode #2 is now positive and the plate of diode #1 is negative. Diode #2 will now conduct and diode #1 will not. The electrons flow through the transformer from B to C, into the load resistor R_L, and back to the cathode of diode #2. They then flow to the plate and back to point B. Notice that the current flows through the load resistor in the same direction as it did previously. Notice, also, that the current flows through the resistor in the same direction during both the positive and negative halves of the input cycle. We have very definitely used both halves of the AC input cycle and have accomplished full-wave rectification. Figure 5-5A shows the AC across the transformer secondary. Figure 5-5B shows the pulsating DC flowing through the load. Compare this output with the rectified wave picture of Figure 5-2B.

VOLTAGE OF HALF-WAVE AND FULL-WAVE RECTIFIERS

In the half-wave rectifier, the entire transformer secondary delivers voltage to the tube. In the full-wave rectifier, only one-half of the transformer secondary delivers voltage to a conducting tube at any one time. This is because the full wave system used a center-tapped transformer. For example: If the full transformer secondary voltage (A to B) is 400 volts (see Figures 5-3 and 5-4), the full 400 volts will appear across the load of the half-wave rectifier, whereas only 200 volts will appear across the load in the full-wave rectifier.

SUMMARY OF RECTIFICATION

(1) A single diode is used as a half-wave rectifier for converting AC to DC. Only half of the input AC wave is used and the full voltage of the secondary of the power transformer is obtained as useful DC output.

(2) A double diode is used as a full-wave rectifier. Both halves of the AC wave are used and greater efficiency is obtained. The output voltage is only half of the total transformer secondary voltage.

FILTERING

Figure 5-6 illustrates the output voltage waveform of a battery. Notice that the voltage output remains constant. It does not vary with time. The output voltage of the battery is pure DC. Remember, this is the type of voltage that the vacuum tubes of a radio require in order to operate properly. Now, look back to Figures 5-2B and 5-5B which show the output wave shapes of a half-wave and full-wave rectifier system. Compare these wave shapes to that of the battery output wave shape.

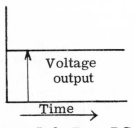

Figure 5-6. Pure DC.

It is evident that the output of the rectifier systems is far from being pure DC. The output is actually a pulsating DC, or a DC with a superimposed AC wave, called a ripple, If we could somehow remove or filter out the AC component or ripple from the pulsating DC, we would end up with a straight line or pure DC. Since we are striving to get a pure DC output from our rectifier system, it is obvious that we are going to have to remove the ripple from the output waveform. The method of removing the ripple from the DC output is known as FILTERING. The device which does the filtering is called a FILTER.

The output waveform of the rectifier is actually a combination of direct current and an AC ripple. The direct current and the AC ripple are called the COMPONENTS of the pulsating wave.

RIPPLE FREQUENCY

The ripple has a very definite fundamental frequency. Examination of Figure 5-2 should indicate to you that the ripple frequency for a half-wave rectifier is the same as the line frequency or 60 CYCLES per second. Recall the definition of frequency, which is the number of times a wave shape repeats itself in one second. Examination of Figure 5-5 should also indicate to you that the ripple frequency for a full-wave rectifier is twice the line frequency or 120 cycles per second.

THE FILTERING SYSTEM

Filtering out the ripple component is accomplished by connecting a filter system to the output of the rectifier tube. A filter system is a circuit consisting of capacitors and inductors. The capacitors are called filter capacitors and the inductors are known as filter chokes.

There are two different types of filter arrangements that are being used in transmitters and receivers. One is the capacitor input type and the other is the choke input type. Both of these filters will now be discussed.

CAPACITOR INPUT FILTER

Figure 5-7 shows a capacitor input filter system connected to the output of a full-wave rectifier. The filter is enclosed within the dashed line. The filter is recognized as a capacitor input type because the filter component nearest to the rectifier is a capacitor (C_1). The complete filter is given the name π filter. π is a Greek letter pronounced "pi". The π filter is the one most commonly found in radio receivers today.

The filter operates to remove the AC component in the follow-

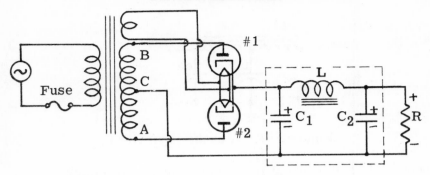

Figure 5-7.   Full-wave rectifier circuit.

ing manner: Point B in Figure 5-8 illustrates the rectified wave

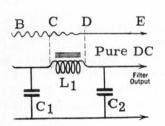

Figure 5-8. Filtering.

shape at the input to the filter. Remember that this wave is a combination of a DC voltage and an AC ripple. Now, C_1 is a very high capacitance capacitor of about 20 ufd. A 20 ufd capacitor has a very low reactance to a 120 cps. ripple component. It will, therefore, short circuit, or by-pass most of the ripple component. The DC voltage, on the other hand, is not affected by the presence of capacitor C_1. Remember that a capacitor acts like an open-circuit to a DC voltage. We say that a capacitor blocks DC. Point C shows the resulting wave shape after it is acted upon by capacitor C_1. Notice that some of the ripple still remains superimposed on the DC wave. The choke, L_1, has a very low DC resistance. The DC will, therefore, pass right through L_1 without any opposition. However, the choke will generate a very strong counter emf. to oppose the AC ripple. The result is that practically all of the remaining ripple will be prevented from passing through the choke. The wave shape appearing on the other side of the choke is shown at point D. The wave shape is practically pure DC, with just a very slight ripple remaining. Capacitor C_2 acts in exactly the same manner as C_1. It will short out the remaining ripple, leaving just the pure DC, as illustrated at point E. The pure DC voltage can now be satisfactorily applied to the vacuum tubes for their proper operation. The DC voltage which is applied to the vacuum tubes is called the B+ voltage.

In AC-DC radio receivers, it is common to use a resistor in place of the filter choke. While the resistor does not work as well as the choke in this application, it takes up less room, is more

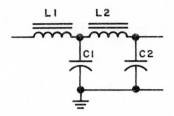

Figure 5-9. A choke input filter.

economical, and does cut down on the amount of ripple.

THE CHOKE INPUT FILTER

Figure 5-9 illustrates a CHOKE INPUT FILTER. We call it a choke input filter because the first filter component after the rectifier is a choke. The filtering action of the choke input filter is similar to that of the capacitor input filter. However, it has an advantage and a disadvantage when compared to a capacitor input filter. The choke input filter has better voltage regulation than a capacitor input filter. (The subject of voltage regulation will be fully discussed in a later paragraph). On the other hand, the capacitor input filter provides a higher output voltage than the choke input filter.

THE ELECTROLYTIC CAPACITOR

The average value of a filter capacitor for a receiver lies in the range between 4 and 50 μfd. At these high values of capacity, the ordinary paper or mica capacitor would be too large in physical size for practical use. A special type of capacitor, called an ELECTROLYTIC CAPACITOR, was designed to have a large value of capacitance in a small size container. The electrolytic capacitor depends on a chemical action to produce a very thin film of oxide which forms the dielectric.

All electrolytic capacitors are polarized; that is, they have a positive and negative terminal. The positive terminal must always be connected to the positive DC voltage point in the circuit, and the negative terminal must similarly be connected to the negative DC point. If these rules are not observed, the capacitor will short-circuit under operation and will have to be replaced. The short-circuit may also damage the rectifier tube.

The principle disadvantages of the electrolytic capacitor are its short life (compared to other capacitors) and its high leakage current. A capacitor is said to have leakage when a small value of DC current flows through its dielectric. In other words, the dielectric is not an absolutely perfect insulator. A good electrolytic capacitor will have a low value of leakage current never exceeding 3 or 4 ma. at its rated working voltage. Electrolytic capacitors are used chiefly in power supplies where leakage current is not important.

The working voltage of an electrolytic capacitor should never be exceeded under actual operation as the capacitor may break down and short-circuit.

THE SHORT-CIRCUITED FILTER CAPACITOR

If capacitor C_1 of Figure 5-7 shorts, the rectifier tube will conduct excessive current. As a result, the safety fuse in series with the primary of the power transformer will blow. The fuse acts as a protective device for the components in the rectifier circuit. If there is no fuse, the plates of the vacuum type rectifier tube will become red hot due to the bombardment of the plate by the large electron flow. The tube may become damaged and will have to be replaced. The primary or secondary windings of the transformer may also burn out due to the excessive current.

If capacitor C_2 in Figure 5-7 were to short, the rectifier tube would conduct very heavily through the choke coil. The choke coil might burn out, in addition to the above-mentioned components.

If either C_1 or C_2 shorts, there obviously will be no B+ voltage and the radio or transmitter will not function.

THE FILTER CHOKE

Filter chokes in a receiver power supply run from 4 to 30 henries. Chokes are designed to have as low a DC resistance as possible. As a result, the DC voltage drop across the choke will be low and the remaining B+ voltage will be as high as possible.

SUMMARY OF FILTERING ACTION

(1) Filtering smooths out the ripple in a rectified DC wave.

(2) A capacitor input filter is used when a high output voltage is desired and where regulation is not too important. Receiver power supplies almost always use capacitor input filters.

(3) A choke input filter is used where regulation is of first importance - as in a transmitter power supply.

(4) The output ripple frequency of a half-wave system is equal to the line frequency of 60 cps. The ripple frequency for the full-wave rectifier is double the line frequency, or 120 cps. For equal filtering action, the filter capacitors in a half-wave power supply should have a greater capacitance than the filter capacitors in a full-wave power supply.

VOLTAGE REGULATION

The load current is the current that is drawn from the power supply by the vacuum tubes of the receiver or transmitter. If the load current varies, the B+ voltage will also vary. The B+ voltage is at a maximum when the load current is zero. As the load on the power supply increases, the B+ voltage drops. At full load current, the B+ voltage is at a minimum. A good power supply is one whose B+ voltage varies very little under varying load conditions. We say that such a power supply has good VOLTAGE REGULATION. A power supply with poor voltage regulation is one whose B+ voltage varies considerably with changes in load conditions. The formula for percentage modulation is:

$$\% \text{ Regulation} = \frac{\text{Emax.} - \text{Emin.}}{\text{Emin.}} \times 100$$

where: Emax. is maximum voltage and Emin is minimum voltage.

The vacuum tubes in a radio receiver draw a constant load current from the power supply. A receiver power supply is, therefore, not required to have good voltage regulation characteristics. A transmitter, on the other hand, presents a varying load to the power supply. The transmitter power supply should, therefore, have good voltage regulation characteristics.

In order to improve the voltage regulation of a power supply, a resistor is often bridged across the output capacitor (resistor R in Figure 5-7). This resistor is known as a BLEEDER RESISTOR. A bleeder resistor improves the voltage regulation by providing a minimum load on the power supply. It also serves to discharge the filter capacitors when the power is turned off.

The bleeder resistor may also be used as a voltage divider to supply different voltages for use in the receiver or transmitter.

ADVANTAGES OF FULL-WAVE OVER HALF-WAVE RECTIFICATION.

The output of a full-wave rectifier is easier to filter than a half-wave rectifier. The reason for this is as follows:

You will recall that the formula for capacitive reactance is:

$$X_c = \frac{1}{2\pi fc}$$

From this formula, we see that the higher the frequency, the lower the reactance of the filter capacitor to the AC component. The ripple frequency of a full-wave rectifier (120 cps.) is twice that of a half-wave rectifier (60 cps.). Because of this, the reactances of the filter capacitors will be one-half as much at 120 cps. as they would be at 60 cps. The filter capacitors will therefore more effectively by-pass or get rid of a 120 cps. ripple than a 60 cps.

ripple.

Also note that the counter-emf. or opposition of the choke is twice as great at 120 cps. as it is at 60 cps. This is because the reactance of an inductor is directly proportional to the frequency. ($X_L = 2\pi fL$).

Thus, we see that the AC ripple of a full-wave rectifier is more easily squelched than the AC ripple of a half-wave rectifier.

Another advantage of full-wave rectification over half-wave rectification is better voltage regulation.

INVERSE PEAK VOLTAGE

A rectifier tube does not conduct during one-half of the input AC cycle. This is when the plate is negative with respect to the cathode. During this non-conducting time, there will be a high negative voltage on the plate. Figure 5-10 illustrates this condition. The voltage across the transformer secondary is 300 volts peak and the input capacitor is charged up to 300 volts from the previous alternation. Notice that the two voltages are in series and in phase across the rectifier tube. The maximum voltage between plate and cathode during non-conduction is 600 volts. This voltage is called the INVERSE PEAK VOLTAGE. If this inverse peak voltage exceeds the rating given by the manufacturer, there is a great danger of damage from an arc-back between the two elements.

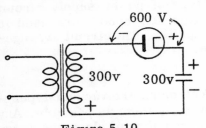

Figure 5-10.
Inverse peak voltage.

THE SOLID-STATE RECTIFIER

In the previous lesson we learned that we have two types of diodes available: the vacuum-tube diode and the semiconductor. Thus, in power supplies we can use either type as a rectifier. Generally, for power supplies, the semiconductors are either selenium or silicon types. The selenium rectifier is actually made up of successive layers of selenium and iron. Both selenium and silicon rectifiers can be designed to handle the large currents of power supplies. The silicon rectifier has an advantage in that it can be made much smaller than the selenium type. Solid-state rectifiers have gradually replaced vacuum tubes as diode rectifiers since they are lighter in weight, do not require a socket, and require no heating power. They are instant starting.

Basically, the circuits using tubes or semiconductors are

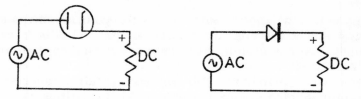

Figure 5-11A.
Vacuum tube diode rectifier.

Figure 5-11B.
Semiconductor type rectifier.

very much alike. Figure 5-11 shows a vacuum tube diode rectifier in drawing A and a semiconductor rectifier in drawing B. The semiconductor can be used in any type of power supply circuit which uses tubes. Thus, you will find semiconductors used in both half-wave and full-wave power supplies. The circuit arrangement of the filters remains the same.

GAS-FILLED TUBES

In general, the tubes used in electronics are vacuum-types - that is, as much of the air is pumped out of them as possible. Any air left in a tube interferes with the free flow of electrons from cathode to plate. If air is present, the collision between the electrons and the atoms of the gases that make up air results in ionization. This means that the atoms may lose one or more electrons. The atoms, minus one or more of their electrons, are known as ions. Having lost an electron, the ions become positively charged and are attracted to the negative cathode. They are much larger and heavier than electrons and therefore, strike the cathode with considerable force. This may ultimately destroy the cathode.

Gases such as neon or argon are sometimes purposely put into specially constructed tubes. These tubes are then known as gas tubes. Figure 5-12 shows a circuit using a gas tube.

The circuit is placed across the output of a power supply, such as the one shown earlier in Figure 5-7. Note that the tube does

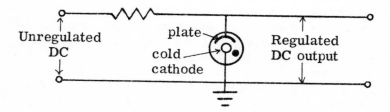

Figure 5-12. Cold cathode gaseous voltage regulator.

not have a filament. It is called a cold-cathode, gaseous diode.
When a positive voltage is applied to the plate of the gas tube, a
few stray electrons migrate toward the plate. These electrons
collide with the gas atoms in the tube and strip one or more electrons from their outer rings, converting them into positive ions.
These ions are attracted to the negative cathode and bombard it.
This striking action warms up the cathode and it starts to release
a few electrons, which are promptly attracted to the plate. Further ionization takes place, with the result that there is continued
bombardment of the cathode and a steady flow of current toward
the plate.

The cold-cathode, gaseous diode is used as a voltage regulator
across power supplies because it can help maintain a constant or
regulated DC output voltage. It does so in the following manner:
Consider the circuit shown in Figure 5-12. If the DC unregulated
voltage should rise, a higher voltage would appear on the plate of
the gas diode and as a result, more current would flow through
it. This increased current has an effect on the ionization of the
tube and causes its resistance to decrease. The result is a reduced voltage drop across the tube, offsetting the increase. In
other words, the voltage across the tube remains constant. On
the other hand, if the unregulated voltage decreases, the voltage
across the diode will decrease and it will draw less current. This
causes the tube's resistance to increase and the voltage across
the tube will also increase. Thus, the fall in voltage will also be
offset. We can therefore see that this circuit tends to keep the
output voltage constant.

Voltage regulator circuits are found in transmitter power supplies and in test equipment because of the need for good voltage
regulation. They are not used in receivers because the ordinary
receiver has no need for them.

THE ZENER DIODE
The Zener diode is a semiconductor that can be used in place
of the gas diode to supply voltage regulation across the output of a

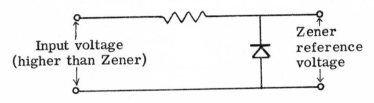

Figure 5-13. A Zener diode.

power supply. A typical circuit is shown in Figure 5-13. Note the similarity between this circuit and the one for the gas diode shown in Figure 5-12. The operation of the Zener diode is similar to that of the cold-cathode gas diode. If the voltage applied to the Zener circuit increases beyond a predetermined point (called the "Zener Knee"), the diode "breaks down" and conducts heavily. At applied voltages greater than the Zener Knee, the voltage drop across the Zener diode will remain constant, regardless of the current variations. This allows the Zener to be used as a constant voltage reference across circuits requiring a constant voltage.

CHAPTER 6

VACUUM TUBES

INTRODUCTION

In Chapter 4, we studied the construction of a diode vacuum tube. In Chapter 5, we studied the action of the diode vacuum tube as a rectifier in changing alternating current to direct current. We will now deal with the operation of the vacuum tube when used as an amplifier. An amplifier increases the amplitude of small voltages or currents. The vacuum tubes that are used for amplification purposes are three, four and five element tubes. The three element tube is called a TRIODE; four and five element tubes are called TETRODES and PENTODES, respectively. We shall now proceed to study each one of these tubes in detail.

THE TRIODE

The TRIODE is different from the diode in that it contains one more element. This new element is called the CONTROL GRID. The control grid is a thin piece of wire wound in the form of a spiral mesh. It surrounds the cathode. Electrons emitted by the cathode can easily pass through the grid structure and onto the plate. Figure 6-1A shows the actual physical arrangement of the cathode, grid and plate structure in a typical triode. Notice that the grid is placed much closer to the cathode than to the plate.

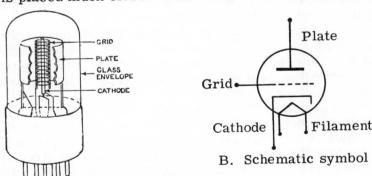

A. Cut away section of a triode

Figure 6-1   The triode.

Figure 6-1B illustrates the schematic representation of the triode. The grid is shown by means of a dashed line between the cathode and plate.

OPERATION OF A TRIODE

Figure 6-2 shows a triode circuit which is used to study the effect of grid voltage variations upon the plate current. The plate current is measured by placing a milliammeter in series with the plate circuit. All tube voltage measurements are taken with the cathode as a reference point.

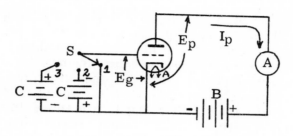

Figure 6-2.   Effect of grid voltage on plate current flow.

Notice the letters A, B and C beneath the battery symbols in Figure 6-2. These letters indicate the voltages that are applied to the different elements in the tube. The "A" voltage is applied to the heater, or filament. The "B" voltage is applied to the plate. The "C" voltage is applied to the grid. "S" is a three-position switch in the control grid circuit. With the switch in position #1, the control grid is connected directly to the cathode. With the switch in position #2, the control grid is connected to the negative terminal of a battery. With the switch in position #3, the control grid is connected to the positive terminal of a battery. Let us see how changes in the control grid voltage affect the operation of the triode. With the switch in position #1 and the plate positive, electrons will flow from the cathode through the grid structure to the plate. Since the grid is connected directly to the cathode, it will not affect the flow of plate current.

If the switch is thrown to position #2, the grid becomes negative with respect to the cathode. The negatively charged grid will repel many of the negatively charged electrons back into the area surrounding the cathode. Hence, the number of electrons which are able to reach the plate is reduced. This effect is illustrated in Figure 6-3. The milliammeter in the plate circuit will show a reduction in the plate current when the grid voltage is changed from a zero voltage to a negative voltage.

If the switch is thrown to position #3, the grid becomes positive with respect to the cathode. The plate current will increase since the positive control grid attracts the negative electrons and allows many more electrons to be drawn to the plate than it did in switch position #1 and #2. A positive grid actually pulls electrons from the cathode to the plate. Thus, we see how the control grid acts as a control valve for plate current flow. As we vary the voltage on the grid, the plate current varies. THE CONTROL GRID, THEREFORE, CONTROLS THE FLOW OF ELECTRONS TO THE PLATE. In normal operation, the control grid usually has a negative voltage on it.

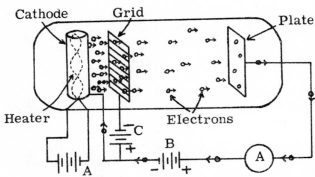

Figure 6-3. Effect of negative grid on plate current flow.

PLATE CURRENT - GRID VOLTAGE CURVE

In order to further study the relationship between the plate current and the grid voltage, let us take measurements to see exactly how the plate current varies with changes in the grid voltage. Figure 6-4 illustrates a schematic of a triode whose grid voltage can be varied by means of a potentiometer placed across the "C" battery. Let us plot the milliammeter plate current readings for different values of grid voltage on a graph. Figure 6-5 illustrates the resulting graph. The horizontal line represents the grid voltage in volts and the vertical line represents the plate current in milliamperes. The plate current measurements are taken with the plate voltage kept constant at 150 volts. If we draw a line through the points that represent the various plate current readings, we obtain a curve known as the Eg-Ip characteristic curve. Notice that if the grid is made sufficiently negative (minus 10 volts), the plate current drops to zero. At this point, the highly negative grid repels all electrons back to the cathode area. As the grid voltage is made less negative (more positive), the electrons begin to flow to the plate. If we continue to make the grid voltage less negative, the plate current will continue to increase. As the grid

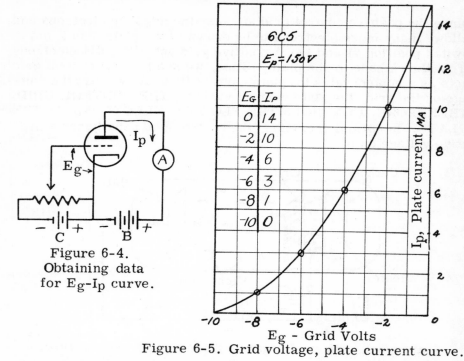

E_G	I_P
0	14
-2	10
-4	6
-6	3
-8	1
-10	0

6C5
$E_p=150V$

Figure 6-4.
Obtaining data
for E_g-I_p curve.

Figure 6-5. Grid voltage, plate current curve.

voltage is made less and less negative, the plate current continues to rise. A point is soon reached (not shown in Figure 6-5) where the plate current can no longer increase, regardless of further increases in positive grid voltage. This point is called the SATURATION POINT.

The voltage that is applied to the grid is called GRID BIAS VOLTAGE, or simply BIAS. The BIAS that cuts the plate current to zero is called the CUT-OFF BIAS. In Figure 6-5, the cut-off bias is -10 volts. Whenever the voltage on the grid prevents current from flowing, we say that we have a BLOCKED GRID.

The curve of Figure 6-5 was obtained with the plate voltage held constant. We can also take data of grid voltage and plate current readings for different values of plate voltage. The result of plotting all these points is a series of curves called a FAMILY OF CURVES, as illustrated in Figure 6-6. Each

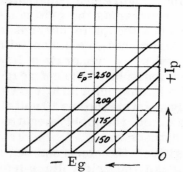

Fig. 6-6. Family of E_g-I_p curves.

curve is plotted with the grid voltage varied while the plate voltage is kept constant. Notice that for a given grid voltage, the plate current increases with increases in plate voltage. This is to be expected, since an increase in plate voltage should result in an increase in plate current.

THE Ep-Ip CHARACTERISTIC CURVE FOR THE TRIODE

In Figure 6-5, the plate voltage was kept constant and plate current readings were plotted as we varied the grid voltage. Another popular characteristic curve is the Ep-Ip curves of Figure 6-7. Here, the grid voltage is kept constant and plate current readings are plotted as we vary the plate voltage. Notice that the plate current rises as the plate voltage increases. The Ep-Ip curves are the ones that are usually found in tube manuals.

THE TRIODE AS AN AMPLIFIER

In a previous paragraph it was stated that multi-element tubes are used to amplify weak signals. We will now proceed to study the exact manner in which a triode amplifies a signal voltage that

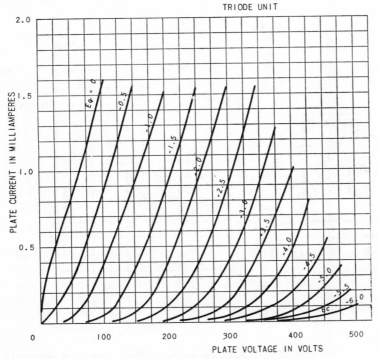

Figure 6-7. Family of E_p-I_p curves.

is applied to its grid.

The control grid is physically much closer to the cathode than the plate is. The grid voltage will, therefore, have a greater effect on the plate current than will the plate voltage. A small change in grid voltage will cause a large change in plate current, whereas a small change in plate voltage causes a small change in plate current. Let us see, graphically, how a changing voltage (such as an AC signal) on the grid of a triode, causes the plate current to vary. Figure 6-8 illustrates a triode whose plate is connected to a fixed B+ voltage. The grid is in series with an AC generator and a fixed bias voltage. The total voltage between the grid and cathode will always be the sum of the generator or signal voltage and the bias voltage.

We will assume that the signal voltage is 1 volt peak and that the battery bias voltage is 3 volts. From the Ip-Eg curve of Figure 6-9, it can be seen that when the AC signal applied to the grid is zero, the plate current will be 8 ma. This is due to the 3 volts of bias supplied by the bias battery. The value of 8 ma. is obtained from the graph by working vertically from the -3 volt point on the grid voltage line until the curve is reached. From this point,

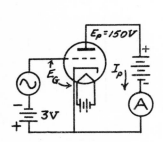

Figure 6-8.
Triode with an AC signal
on the grid.

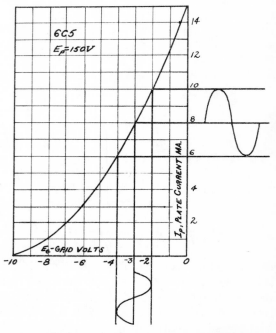

Figure 6-9. Plate current wave-form
resulting from an AC grid voltage.

we go straight across until we hit the vertical plate current line., In this case, we reach the vertical line at 8 ma.

Let us see what happens on the positive half of the AC signal when +1 volt is being applied to the grid. Since the signal voltage of +1 volt and -3 volts of bias are in series, the resultant voltage between the grid and cathode will be -2 volts (the sum of +1 and -3 is -2). By looking at Figure 6-9, we see that -2 volts on the grid causes a plate current of 10 ma. Thus, when the incoming signal reaches its positive peak value of +1 volt, the plate current rises to 10 ma.

On the negative half of the incoming signal, -4 volts will appear between the grid and cathode. This is because the sum of the -1 volt of signal and the -3 volts of bias is -4 volts. By looking at the graph, it can be seen that -4 volts on the grid causes a plate current of 6 ma. Thus, when the incoming signal reaches its negative peak value of -1 volt, the plate current drops to 6 ma.

From the above, we can see that the plate current rises and falls in step with the signal on the grid. As a matter of fact, the waveform of the plate current variation is an exact reproduction of the signal that is applied to the grid.

Thus far, we have converted grid voltage variations into plate current variations. In order to make use of these plate current variations, some device must be placed in the plate circuit to act as a load across which the varying plate current will develop a varying voltage. The plate load may be a resistor, an inductor or a tuned circuit. Figure 6-10 shows a resistor used as a plate load

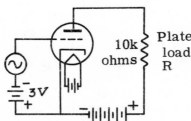

Figure 6-10. Triode using a resistor as a plate load.

in a triode amplifier circuit. Except for the plate load resistor, this circuit is the same as that in Figure 6-8. From Figure 6-9, we can see that a 1 volt signal caused a total plate current variation of 4 milliamperes (from 6 to 10 ma.). This 4 ma. variation will cause a total voltage variation of 40 volts to be produced across the 10,000 ohm resistor. This can easily be proven by Ohm's law. One form of Ohm's law states that:

$$E = I \times R \qquad E = .004 \times 10,000 \qquad E = 40 \text{ V}.$$

Thus it can be seen that a 2 volt AC signal variation (from -2 volts to -4 volts peak to peak) can produce a 40 volt variation in the plate circuit. In other words, the original signal or variation that was applied to the grid has been AMPLIFIED twenty times. ($\frac{40}{2} = 20$)

From Figure 6-9, it can be seen that the voltage variation in the plate circuit is not only amplified, but it is also a faithful reproduction of the grid signal. The circuit in Figure 6-10 is therefore the basis for all amplification circuits in radio and television.

VACUUM TUBE CHARACTERISTICS

Since many different types of vacuum tubes are used in radio and television circuits, it is important to classify tubes according to the performance which may be expected of them. The three most important factors by which tubes are classified are the AMPLIFICATION FACTOR, the TRANSCONDUCTANCE and the PLATE RESISTANCE.

(1) Amplification Factor. The AMPLIFICATION FACTOR of a tube is the maximum voltage amplification which can be expected from the tube. It is a theoretical value never reached in actual circuit use. Stated mathematically, it is the ratio of the change in plate voltage to the change in grid voltage that produces the same change in plate current. For example, let us assume that a certain tube is operating with a plate voltage of 250 volts, a grid voltage of -10 volts and a plate current of 18 ma. Let us assume that if we should change the plate voltage to 280 volts and leave the grid voltage constant, the plate current would go up to 23 ma. This means that a plate voltage change of 30 volts results in a plate current change of 5 ma. Suppose that a grid voltage change from -10 volts to -13 volts returns the plate current from 23 ma. back to 18 ma. We can say that a grid voltage change of 3 volts has the same effect on the plate current as a plate voltage change of 30 volts. The amplification factor would, therefore, be the plate voltage change (30 volts) divided by the grid voltage change (3 volts) or 10.

The amplification factor is commonly designated by the Greek letter μ. The formula for the μ, or mu, of a tube is:

(6-1) Amplification factor $(\mu) = \dfrac{\Delta \text{Ep}}{\Delta \text{Eg}}$

The terms ΔEp and ΔEg mean a small change in plate voltage and a small change in grid voltage, respectively.

(2) Transconductance. The TRANSCONDUCTANCE or MUTUAL CONDUCTANCE of a tube is the figure of merit of the tube.

It tells us how much of a plate current variation we can get for a certain amount of grid voltage variation. Transconductance is defined as the ratio of a small change in plate current to the change in grid voltage that produced it. The formula for transconductance is:

(6-2)   Transconductance (Gm) = $\dfrac{\triangle Ip}{\triangle Eg}$

where: $\triangle Ip$ is a small change in plate current.
         $\triangle Eg$ is the small change in grid voltage that caused $\triangle Ip$.
         Gm is the symbol for transconductance.

The basic unit of the transconductance of a tube is the MHO. The mho was previously mentioned in Chapter 1 as the unit of conductance. We use the same unit because the transconductance of a tube is similar to the conductance of a circuit.

(3) Plate Resistance. The PLATE RESISTANCE of a tube is the internal resistance between the cathode and plate to the flow of a varying plate current. Mathematically speaking, it is the ratio of a small change in plate voltage to the change in plate current that this voltage change produces. The formula for plate resistance is:

(6-3) Plate Resistance (Rp) = $\dfrac{\triangle Ep}{\triangle Ip}$

A tube may be considered to be a variable resistor in its operation as an amplifier. If the grid is made positive, the current flow from cathode to plate is increased. This means that the resistance from the cathode to the plate is now less than it was before. On the other hand, if the grid is made more negative, the plate current will decrease. This means, of course, that the plate resistance has become greater.

PLATE IMPEDANCE

Since we have both resistance and capacitance between the plate and the cathode, the total opposition to the flow of current is impedance. However, for most purposes, the impedance is regarded as being equal to the plate resistance.

EFFICIENCY OF VACUUM TUBES

We often use the term EFFICIENCY when we speak about the performance of a certain device or machine. Efficiency refers to the amount of power that can be gotten out of a device, as compared to the amount of power that has been put into it. For instance, if 100 watts of electrical power is used up in a light bulb and only 2 watts of equivalent light power is produced, we can say that the electric bulb is a low efficiency device. The bulb generates into light only 2% of the power that is put into it. (The other 98 watts are dissipated inside the bulb in the form of heat). On the other hand, an electric motor may draw 100 watts of electric power and produce 75 watts of equivalent mechanical power. We can say that the motor is a high efficiency device. The motor produces, in the form of useful work, 75% of the power put into it.

In radio, we classify vacuum tubes according to their efficiency in delivering useful power to a load.

The plate efficiency of a vacuum tube is defined as the ratio of the AC plate power output to the DC plate power input. It is given in a percentage, and its mathematical formula is:

$$(6\text{-}3) \quad \text{Plate Efficiency (in \%)} = \frac{\text{AC output power}}{\text{DC input power}} \times 100$$

For example, if the AC power output of a vacuum tube is 150 watts and the DC power input is 200 watts, the efficiency is 150 divided by 200 or 0.75. We change this to a percentage by multiplying the answer by 100. Thus, 0.75 x 100 = 75%.

The AC power output of a tube is the power in watts that the tube delivers to its load. The load may be the loudspeaker or the grid of a following tube. The DC power input, on the other hand, is the product of the DC plate voltage applied to the tube and the DC plate current. For instance, if the plate voltage is 750 volts and the plate current is 150 milliamperes, then the power input is 112.5 watts. The power input is derived in the following manner:

Power input in watts = Ep x Ip
P input = 750 x .15　　　　　P = 112.5 watts

Note that the 150 milliamperes was changed to amperes by moving the decimal three places to the left.

MAXIMUM PLATE DISSIPATION

In the above problem concerning the plate efficiency of a vacuum tube, it is apparent that only a certain percentage of the applied power (input power) appears as output power. What happened to the remainder of the input power? The remainder of the input power is wasted in the form of heat within the tube, exactly as in a light bulb. Remember that the tube represents a resistance between the cathode and plate. Power loss applies to the resistance of a tube, as well as any ordinary resistor. The plate current, in flowing through the plate resistance, dissipates heat. The power dissipated on the plate in the form of heat is equal to Ip^2Rp, where Ip is the plate current and Rp is the plate resistance.

There is a limit to the amount of power that a tube can dissipate in the form of heat without damaging itself. This limit is known as the **MAXIMUM PLATE DISSIPATION** and it is expressed in watts. To find the maximum plate dissipation for any particular tube, we simply look it up in the tube manual.

LIMITATIONS OF A TRIODE

In the early days of radio, triodes were used exclusively in radio receivers and transmitters. Later on, the tetrodes and pentodes made their appearance and replaced the triode in many applications. The reason for this change was that the triode had certain characteristics which limited its application in radio work. Before we discuss the tetrode and pentode, we shall first examine in detail the limitations of the triode.

In Chapter 3, we learned that two conducting surfaces, separated by an insulator, form a capacitor. Since the plate and grid of a tube are two conducting surfaces separated by a vacuum dielectric, there exists a capacitance between the plate and grid. By the same reasoning, a capacitor is formed between the grid and cathode, and between the plate and cathode. These internal tube capacitances are called INTERELECTRODE CAPACITANCES. The interelectrode capacitance between the plate and the grid exerts a detrimental effect upon the action of a triode amplifier. This capacitance gives rise to a condition known as OSCILLATION which is extremely undesirable. Oscillations come about in the following manner: A varying grid voltage causes a varying plate voltage, which is then passed on to the next stage. However, because of the undesirable grid to plate capacitance, the voltage variations from the plate circuit are FED BACK to the grid circuit and are reamplified until oscillations or howling takes place. This is especially true at radio frequencies. In a later chapter, we will discuss this condition of oscillation in greater detail.

Another defect of the triode results from the fact that the plate current depends not only upon the grid voltage, but also upon the plate voltage. Because of this, the gain of a triode, used as an amplifier, is kept down. For example, a positive grid signal will cause the plate current to go up; the increasing Ip will increase the voltage across the load resistor. The voltage across the load resistor and the voltage between plate and cathode are in series and therefore, must always add up to the fixed B+ voltage value. If the voltage across the load resistor goes up, the plate voltage must go down. The decreased plate voltage will, in turn, cause the plate current to decrease somewhat, counteracting the effect of the signal on the plate current. Thus the amplification is kept down. The way to circumvent this defect would be to make the plate current independent of the plate voltage. Variations in plate voltage would then have no effect on the plate current. This is achieved in the tetrode and pentode.

THE TETRODE

In an effort to reduce the grid-plate capacitance within the tube, a fourth element was added to the conventional triode. This fourth element is called a SCREEN GRID; the screen grid is placed between the control grid and the plate. The top view of a tetrode is shown in Figure 6-11A; the schematic symbol of a tetrode is shown in Figure 6-11B. The screen is wound in the form of a spiral grid, similar to the control grid. The screen grid shields the control grid from the plate and thereby reduces the grid-plate capacitance.

In order for the screen grid to act as an effective shield, it must be grounded for AC. But, as we shall soon see, the screen grid must, at the same time, be kept at a high positive DC potential. The way to satisfy both conditions is to ground the screen grid through a capacitor (c of Figure 6-12).

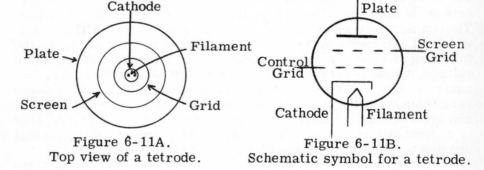

Figure 6-11A.
Top view of a tetrode.

Figure 6-11B.
Schematic symbol for a tetrode.

A typical screen grid, or tetrode (four element) tube connected in a circuit, is shown in Figure 6-12. The screen grid is operated at a DC potential somewhat lower than that of the plate. The positive screen grid acts like the plate of a triode in attracting electrons emitted by the cathode. A few of the electrons will hit the screen grid, resulting in screen current flow. The screen current flows through resistor R1. R1 is called the screen voltage dropping resistor. The screen current that flows through R1 causes a voltage drop across it. The screen grid voltage is therefore the B+ voltage, minus the voltage drop across the resistor R1. The screen voltage is measured from the screen grid to the cathode.

Since the screen grid is similar to the control grid in construction, most of the electrons will pass through the screen and reach the plate. Since the plate is a solid element and more pos-

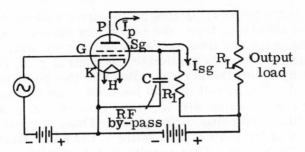

Figure 6-12. Tetrode amplifier circuit.

itive than the screen grid, it will receive most of the electrons emitted by the cathode.

INCREASED AMPLIFICATION OF TETRODE

Because the screen grid is closer to the cathode than the plate, the screen grid has practically complete control over the plate current. The plate current is therefore not influenced by plate voltage variations. Since the screen is at AC ground potential, there will be no variation in the screen voltage when an AC signal is being applied to the grid. The screen grid, therefore, exerts a constant pull on the electrons that make up the plate current. The only element in the tetrode that causes the plate current to vary is the control grid. The control grid no longer shares its control over the plate current with the plate, as it did in the triode. Small variations of voltage on the control grid will cause the plate current to vary without any counteraction from a varying plate voltage. As a result, the plate resistance and the amplification factor of the tetrode are much greater than they are in a triode.

THE PENTODE

The introduction of the screen grid in the tetrode successfully reduced the plate-grid capacitance and increased the amplification factor. The tetrode, however, suffers from one important defect. This defect is known as SECONDARY EMISSION. The pentode (five element tube) was developed to overcome the effects of secondary emission.

Secondary emission is the condition that arises when the high velocity electrons strike the plate. The force of the impact causes additional electrons to be knocked out of the atomic structure of the plate. For every electron that strikes the plate, two or three electrons will be knocked out of the plate. In a triode, these secondary emission electrons normally find their way back to the highly positive plate and cause no interference in the operation of the tube. In the tetrode, as long as the plate voltage is much higher than the screen voltage, the secondary emission electrons fall back to the plate and tube operation will be normal. However, if a large signal voltage is applied to the control grid, the plate voltage will drop below the screen voltage at the positive peak of the input signal. The result of this lowered plate voltage is to cause the secondary emission electrons to flow to the positive screen grid instead of returning to the plate. Thus, the number of electrons reaching the plate drops, while at the same time, the screen current is increased. This results in a reduction in the amplification of the tube and distortion in its output.

In the pentode, a third grid is placed between the screen grid and the plate (see Figure 6-13). The third grid is similar in physical construction to the screen grid and the control grid. This third grid is connected to the cathode, either internally or externally, so that it will be highly negative with respect to the plate and will force the secondary emission electrons back to the plate. Because it suppresses secondary emission, the third grid is called the SUPPRESSOR GRID. The negative suppressor grid will not interfere with the flow of electrons from the cathode to the plate, even though it does suppress the secondary electrons coming from the plate. The reason for this is that the electrons from the cathode are traveling at such a high velocity when they reach the vicinity of the suppressor grid that they go right on through to the highly positive plate. On the other hand, the secondary electrons coming from the plate are moving at a rather low velocity and are easily pushed back to the plate. Figure 6-14 illustrates a pentode hooked up as an amplifier. Note that the only difference between this circuit and the tetrode amplifier circuit of Figure 6-12 is the addition of the suppressor grid.

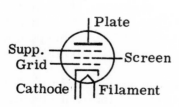

Figure 6-13.
Schematic symbol for pentode.

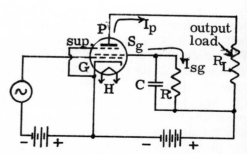

Figure 6-14.
Pentode amplifier circuit.

THE BEAM POWER TUBE

A beam power tube is a pentode with special construction features. A beam power tube has greater power handling ability than the ordinary tetrode or pentode. With very small grid voltages, a beam power tube can develop large amounts of power in its plate circuit. The tube is therefore said to have high power sensitivity. The beam power tube is constructed so that the wire turns of the control grid and screen grid line up with each other horizontally. This means that every turn of the screen grid mesh is directly behind a turn of the control grid mesh. Thus, electrons flowing from the cathode travel through the control grid and onto the plate without striking the screen grid. The screen grid current is therefore very low and, since the plate gets the electrons which would normally have gone to the screen grid, the plate power output is increased. Because of the physical alignment of the control grid and the screen grid, the electrons flow to the plate in sheets, or beams. This is illustrated in Figure 6-15. To further concentrate and form the heavy beams of plate current, deflecting plates are incorporated into the tube structure. These deflecting plates are

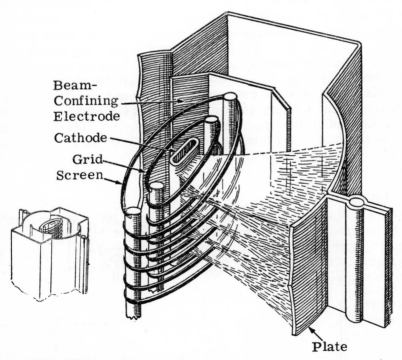

Beam-
Confining
Electrode

Cathode

Grid

Screen

Plate

Figure 6-15. The beam power tube. (Courtesy RCA)

placed between the screen grid and the plate, and extend partway around the tube. These beam forming deflecting plates are internally connected to the cathode and, therefore, acquire a negative charge with respect to the plate. As a result, the deflecting plates repel the electrons into concentrated heavy beams of plate current.

No actual suppressor grid is necessary because secondary emission from the plate is suppressed by the space charge which forms between the plate and screen grid. This space charge has been indicated by the heavier dashes in Figure 6-15. The space charge of the electron beam is caused by the slowing up of electrons in the area between the screen grid and the plate. By operating the plate of the beam power tube at a lower potential than the screen grid, the plate is made negative with respect to the screen. The electrons are therefore slowed down when they pass through the screen on their way to the plate. Stray secondary emission electrons cannot return to the screen grid outside of the beam area because of the beam forming plates. Some beam power tubes use an actual suppressor grid in place of the space charge effect.

To summarize, we can say that the beam power tube has:

(1) high power sensitivity.
(2) high power output.
(3) high plate efficiency.

GAS IN A VACUUM TUBE

The ordinary vacuum type tube is supposed to be free of any gas or air. If a vacuum tube does contain gas which was not excluded during the manufacturing process, it is called a SOFT tube. The visible indication of a soft tube is a red or purple haze, sometimes accompanied by a reddened plate. The plate current of a soft tube is excessively high. A soft tube is often erratic in its operation and should be replaced.

GAS TUBES

Not all tubes are vacuum types. Some have gases such as neon or argon (or a mixture of these gases) put inside the tube and therefore, are known as gas tubes. Gas tubes are used in various applications. For example, they are used as voltage regulators in power supplies.

THE GETTER

Most vacuum tubes contain a GETTER. A getter is a small piece of metal, made of barium or some similar chemical. This chemical removes or destroys stray gases that remain in the vacuum tube after the evacuation process.

CHAPTER 7

TRANSISTORS

THE TRANSISTOR

From what we have learned about tubes in the previous chapter, we know that we can make a diode into a triode by adding a new element called the control grid. This single, added electrode makes a tremendous difference, for the triode tube can amplify, whereas the diode cannot. Thus, it was the triode that advanced receivers from the headphone state to speaker operation.

In a similar manner, semiconductor triodes that amplify can be made from the semiconductor diodes previously described. Figure 7-1 illustrates a pair of P-N diodes placed back to back. The drawing shows that the two diodes have been pushed together.

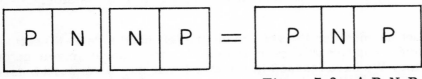

Figure 7-1.
Two diodes - A P-N and an N-P.

Figure 7-2. A P-N-P
transistor from two diodes.

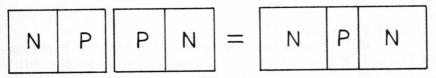

Figure 7-3.
An N-P-N transistor from two diodes.

Combining the two diodes of Figure 7-1 gives us the unit shown in Figure 7-2. We still have our pair of semiconductor diodes for we can divide the combined center or N section into two parts. Figure 7-2 is known as a transistor. The transistor of Figure 7-2 is called a P-N-P type. However, if we go back to our two diodes of Figure 7-1 and turn them around, we can have the two N-sections on the outside and the two P-sections joining each other. In this case, the transistor would be an N-P-N type. Figure 7-3 shows the N-P-N type.

BIASING THE TRANSISTOR

The DC voltages applied to the transistor are known as bias voltages. Figure 7-4 shows the bias voltages on a P-N-P transistor. Note that we have named the three parts of the transistor -- Emitter, Base and Collector. Their vacuum tube equivalents are Cathode, Control Grid and Plate, respectively.

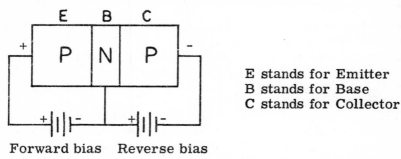

E stands for Emitter
B stands for Base
C stands for Collector

Forward bias   Reverse bias

Figure 7-4.   Method of biasing a P-N-P transistor.

Let us consider the voltage on the left hand side P-N section. We have a positive voltage on the emitter and a negative voltage on the base. We have learned in Chapter 4 that this is forward biased and a current will flow through this section. From our previous discussion in Chapter 4, we can see that the right hand side N-P section is reverse biased and very little current flows in this section.

THE TRANSISTOR CIRCUIT

Figure 7-5 illustrates the electron flow in a basic N-P-N transistor circuit. Section EB is forward biased, while section BC is reverse biased. Electrons from the negative terminal of battery Ee flow into the emitter. From the emitter it would normally be expected that all the electrons leaving Ee would drift into the P section (the base) and return to the positive terminal of Ee. This does not happen. Very few electrons return to Ee through the base. The reason for this is that the base is actually made up of a very thin slice of P-type material. Therefore, we have very few positive "holes" present. This being the case, there are very few "holes" to combine with the electrons and propel them to the positive terminal of Ee. On the other hand, batteries Ee and Ec are series aiding and they give us a high voltage that forces the electrons from the emitter, through the base (P), into the collector and on to the positive terminal of Ec. The approximate electron

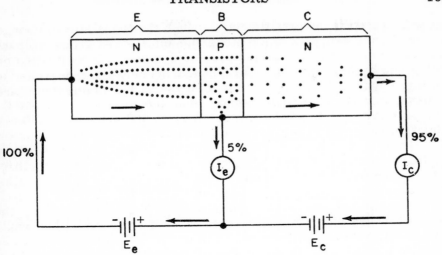

Figure 7-5.   Electron flow in a transistor.

distribution is shown in percentages in Figure 7-5.

It is important to note that while very little current goes into the base to return to Ee, the voltage across EB (Ee) is a large factor in determining the total current flow in the circuit.   This is analagous to the vacuum tube where very little current enters the grid circuit, but where the control grid voltage is a large factor in determining or controlling the plate current.

Let us see how a transistor is able to amplify.   Figure 7-6 is the same as Figure 7-5, except that an AC signal voltage has been inserted and resistors have been added.   The AC signal voltage is now in series with Ee and the signal will alternately add and subtract from the battery voltage. As noted above, this changing volt-

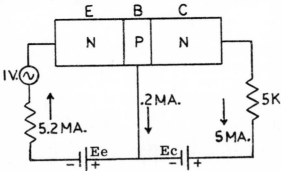

Figure 7-6.   Electron flow in a transistor.

age will cause the current flowing through the transistor to change.

In Figure 7-6, 5.2 ma. enters the emitter. Of this amount, 0.2 ma. returns to Ee via the base and 5.0 ma. travels to the collector and back to Ee. This current will increase and decrease as the signal varies. Let us assume that the signal is one volt, peak to peak, and let us further assume that the AC signal causes the collector current to vary from 4.0 ma. to 6.0 ma. This 2.0 ma. variation causes a 10 volt variation across the 5,000 ohm resistor. (E = IR, E = .002 A. x 5,000 = 10 volts). Thus, we can see how the transistor amplifier stage took a 1.0 volt signal and amplified it ten times to a 10 volt signal. This is similar to the explanation of a vacuum tube amplifier described in Page 92.

We could get the same results using a P-N-P transistor, the only difference being that the batteries being used for bias would have to be reversed. The current in an N-P-N circuit flows in an opposite direction to that of a P-N-P circuit, but other than this, both circuits work in exactly the same way.

TRANSISTOR SYMBOLS

Figure 7-7 shows the same circuit as that of Figure 7-6. However, the transistor pictorial has been replaced with the transistor symbol. There are two transistor symbols; one for P-N-P types and the other for N-P-N. The symbol in Figure 7-7 is that of an N-P-N transistor. The P-N-P symbol is exactly the same, except that the arrow for the emitter points inward. The letters E, B and C represent the emitter, base and collector, respectively.

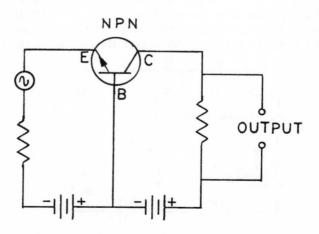

Figure 7-7. A basic transistor amplifier circuit.

CHAPTER 8

AUDIO AMPLIFICATION

INTRODUCTION

At this point, we understand that when a small amplitude signal is applied to the grid of a triode or pentode, it will be amplified and will appear many times larger in the plate circuit. This property of grid-controlled vacuum tubes makes possible their use as AMPLIFIERS. An amplifier may be defined as a device which transforms a small input signal into a large output signal.

AMPLIFIER APPLICATION

Amplifiers find many practical applications. For example, the signal that is developed in the crystal pickup of a record player is much too weak to be applied directly to a speaker. This weak signal must first be amplified (made larger) before it can properly drive a speaker. A lecturer addressing an audience in a large auditorium must have his voice amplified in order for him to be heard by everyone in the hall. The amplifier that accomplishes this is called a PUBLIC ADDRESS SYSTEM. Amplifiers are also extensively used in fields such as motion pictures, electrical recording and photo-electronics. Since amplifiers find such a wide application, it is important that we thoroughly understand their operation.

AMPLIFIERS USED IN RADIO RECEIVERS

The modern radio receiver uses two types of amplifier in its operation. They are:

(1) The radio-frequency (RF) amplifier. This amplifier amplifies the weak radio-frequency signals picked up by the antenna of the receiver. A radio frequency signal is a high frequency radio wave (usually above 400 kilocycles (kc.) which is sent out into space by the radio transmitter. RF amplifiers will be discussed in a later chapter.

(2) The audio-frequency (AF) amplifier. This amplifier amplifies the sound frequencies or audio frequencies before they are applied to the speaker. Audio frequencies are in the range between 16 cps (16 Hz) and approximately 20,000 cps (20,000 Hz).

CLASSIFICATION OF AMPLIFIERS

Amplifiers are classified according to the work they are in-

105

tended to perform and the manner in which they are operated. The classification is determined by the grid bias of the amplifier which, in turn, determines the manner in which they will operate. Amplifiers are classified into general categories - Class A, Class B and Class C. The audio amplifier is invariably operated either Class A or Class B. The Class C amplifier is generally found in a transmitter and will be discussed fully in the chapter on transmitters. There is also a Class AB amplifier which has characteristics midway between those of a Class A amplifier and a Class B amplifier.

CLASS A AMPLIFICATION

A graphical illustration of Class A amplification is shown in Figure 8-1. Figure 8-1 is actually a plate current-grid voltage characteristic curve of the Class A amplifier. The bias voltage or operating point is at the mid-point of the straight line portion of the curve. Because the tube is operated on the straight line portion of the curve, the PLATE CURRENT VARIATIONS ARE AN EXACT REPRODUCTION OF THE INPUT SIGNAL. Thus, we see that Class A operation gives us excellent fidelity.

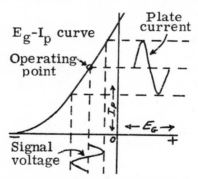

Figure 8-1. Class A operation.

From Figure 8-1, you will notice that plate current flows for the entire cycle of the input signal. In other words, the tube conducts current continuously. Because of this, there is plate dissipation all the time. This results in POOR EFFICIENCY AND LOW POWER OUTPUT.

Other characteristics of a Class A amplifier are:

(1) The signal never drives the grid negative enough to cut the tube off.

(2) The signal never drives the grid positive with respect to the cathode. A positive grid would result in grid current flow,

which would cause distortion. Thus, there is no grid current flow in a Class A amplifier.

THE BIAS VOLTAGE SUPPLY

Practically all amplifiers operate with a certain amount of bias voltage. The two methods of obtaining bias voltage for an AF amplifier are: (1) fixed bias and (2) self-bias, or cathode bias.

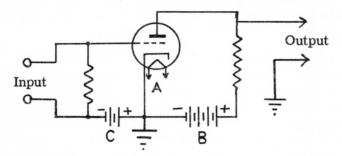

Figure 8-2. Amplifier stage using fixed bias.

Figure 8-2 illustrates an amplifier with fixed bias. The fixed bias in this case is obtained from a source called a "C" battery. The fixed bias voltage can also be obtained from a negative DC voltage point in the power supply. The bias voltage is of constant value and cannot vary. The disadvantage of fixed bias operation is that an external source of power is required.

Figure 8-3 illustrates an amplifier with cathode bias. The biasing circuit consists of the resistor, R, and the capacitor, C, connected from cathode to ground. The bias voltage is developed by the DC plate current flowing from ground through the resistor to the cathode. Since the current flows into the resistor from ground, this side of the resistor is negative with respect to the cathode side. The purpose of the capacitor, C, is to by-pass the AC component of plate current around the resistor. If the AC component of current were allowed to flow through the biasing resistor, a varying bias voltage would be developed. Under normal amplifier operation, this is not desirable. The AC component of plate current therefore flows through the bypass capacitor, C, while the DC component of plate current flows through the biasing resistor, R, establishing a source of bias

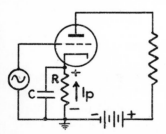

Fig. 8-3. Cathode-bias.

voltage. The advantage of cathode bias is that it eliminates the need for a separate source of bias voltage. Most receiver circuits use this self-biasing principle.

It may sometimes be necessary to compute the value of the biasing resistor, R. For example: Suppose we wish to operate a certain tube as a Class A amplifier. The tube manual states that for Class A operation, the bias for that tube is -3 volts and the plate current will be 10 ma. (.01A). Since we know the voltage across the resistor and the current through it, we can easily find the value of the cathode resistor by using Ohm's law:

$$Rk = \frac{E}{I} = \frac{3}{.01} = 300 \text{ ohms}$$

COUPLING SYSTEMS IN AMPLIFIERS

Audio amplifiers are usually classified according to the method of coupling the signal from one stage to another. There are two common types of AF coupling used in receivers and transmitters. One is transformer coupling and the other is resistance-capacitance coupling.

TRANSFORMER COUPLED AMPLIFIER

A simple transformer coupled audio-amplifier is shown in Figure 8-4. V1 and V2 are the voltage amplifiers. T1 is a special type of matching transformer, known as an audio interstage transformer. For maximum power transfer from the plate of V1 to the grid of V2, the transformer is so designed that its primary impedance approximately matches the plate circuit impedance of V1, and its secondary impedance matches the grid circuit impedance of V2. The turns ratio for this type of transformer is usually 1 to 3 step up from plate to grid. The secondary therefore has about three times as many turns as the primary.

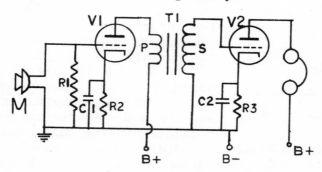

Figure 8-4.   Two-stage transformer-coupled amplifier.

Coupling is accomplished in the following manner: The varying plate current of V1 (which is a replica of the audio signal) generates a varying magnetic field about the primary of transformer T1. This varying magnetic field, in turn, induces a voltage in the secondary of T1 which is applied as a signal voltage to the grid of V2. This signal is then amplified by V2 and applied to the headphones.

Let us now discuss the functions of the other parts of Figure 8-4.

"M" is the microphone which supplies the input signal to the grid of V1.

"R1" is the grid return resistor which serves two purposes:

(a) The microphone changes sound energy to electrical energy. The microphone produces an alternating voltage which is impressed across R1. This alternating voltage is the signal which is to be amplified.

(b) Electrons which collect on the grid can leak off to ground through the resistor. These electrons might otherwise accumulate sufficiently on the grid to cause the tube to cut-off. This condition is known as a blocked grid.

"R2" is a cathode biasing resistor chosen to provide the correct tube bias for Class A operation.

"C1" is a cathode by-pass capacitor. It provides a very low-impedance path around the bias resistor for the audio currents.

"T1" is the interstage audio transformer.

"R3" is a cathode bias resistor.

"C2" is a cathode by-pass capacitor.

ADVANTAGES OF TRANSFORMER COUPLING

The advantages of transformer coupling are:

(1) High gain due to step-up ratio of transformer.

(2) Low DC resistance of transformer primary permits the use of a low B+ voltage.

DISADVANTAGES OF TRANSFORMER COUPLING

The disadvantages of transformer coupling are:

(1) Distortion of the signal due to the transformer characteristics. An amplifier which reproduces faithfully and amplifies equally the band of audio frequencies which is applied to its input is said to have low distortion or HIGH FIDELITY. The average transformers used in a transformer-coupled amplifier introduce some distortion into the signal. As a result, the amplifier is said to have POOR FIDELITY. High fidelity transformer-coupled amplifiers are very difficult to design and therefore, are quite ex-

pensive.

(2) The transformers are large and expensive.

(3) The transformers must be magnetically shielded to prevent pick-up of hum.

(4) Transformer coupling is usually limited to triode amplifiers with the result that the high gain of pentodes cannot be realized.

Transformer coupling is commonly used to couple an output tube to a speaker. Transformer coupling is also commonly used in transistor receivers to couple one transistor stage to the next.

RESISTANCE-CAPACITANCE (R-C) COUPLED AMPLIFIER

The disadvantages of the transformer-coupled amplifier are overcome in the design of a resistance-capacitance coupled amplifier. The major difference between the two amplifiers is that the interstage coupling transformer is replaced with a resistance-capacitance coupling network. The elimination of the transformer allows us to use pentode tubes, with a consequent increase in the overall gain of the amplifier. The elimination of the audio-coupling transformer also does away with the distortion associated with its use. Generally speaking, the R-C amplifier is the superior of the two amplifiers because of its simplicity, compactness, lower cost and higher fidelity.

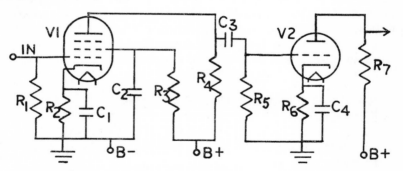

Figure 8-5. Two stage resistance-coupled amplifier.

Figure 8-5 illustrates a two stage, resistance-coupled amplifier. The coupling between the plate of V1 and the grid of V2 consists of a resistance-capacitance network (R4, C3 and R5). Capacitor "C3" is the COUPLING capacitor. Its function is to pass the audio from the plate of V1 to the grid of V2 while, at the same time, blocking the positive plate voltage of V1 from being applied to the grid of V2. If the coupling capacitor becomes shorted, the DC plate voltage of V1 would be applied directly to the grid of V2. The positive voltage on the grid of V2 would result in excessive grid and plate current flow, and would cause the audio signal to become distorted and could cause the tube to burn out. The capacitance of C3 is determined by the reactance it should have for the lowest audio frequency that it is to pass on to the grid of V2. This reactance should be very low for the lowest audio frequency that is to be passed. The AC signal from V1 is developed across R5.

The following is a review summary of the functions of the remaining components in Figure 8-5:

Parts	Function
R1	Grid return resistor
C1, C4	Cathode by-pass capacitors
R2, R6	Cathode bias resistors
R3	Screen dropping resistor
C2	Screen by-pass capacitor
R7	Plate load resistor; high resistance for audio.

FREQUENCY RESPONSE

An amplifier is said to have a FLAT FREQUENCY RESPONSE if it amplifies all frequencies applied to the input grid equally. A frequency response curve is a graph which plots the amplifier voltage output in either volts or decibels over a frequency range. Figure 8-6 illustrates the response curves for a transformer-coupled audio amplifier and a resistance-coupled audio amplifier. The R-C amplifier has the flatter curve and has, therefore, a flatter frequency response. A flatter response means better fidelity.

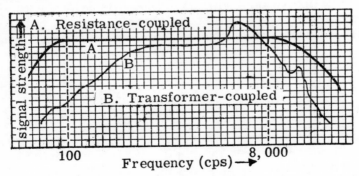

Figure 8-6. Frequency response curve.

DISTORTION IN A CLASS A AMPLIFIER

Figure 8-7A illustrates a pure sine wave of a certain frequency. A pure sine wave is an AC wave which is free of distortion. The ideal audio amplifier is one which will amplify a sine wave

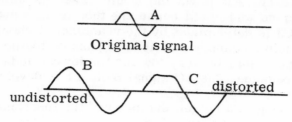

Figure 8-7.   Distortion in Class A amplifier.

without changing its waveshape. The amplified plate signal must therefore be an exact duplicate of the grid signal. Figure 8-7B illustrates an amplified version of the sine wave of Figure 8-7A. It has the same waveshape as Figure 8-7A and therefore, is still considered a pure sine wave (undistorted), even though it is amplified. Figure 8-7C illustrates a distorted sine wave. Note the flattening at the top of the positive portion of the wave.

CAUSES OF DISTORTION IN CLASS A AMPLIFIERS
    Figure 8-8 illustrates the Eg-Ip curve for a properly operated Class A amplifier. The bias point, "A", is at the mid-point of the linear portion of the curve. The input signal is of the correct amplitude and the plate signal is an amplified and undistorted version of the input signal.
    The causes of distortion in a Class A amplifier are as follows:
    (1) Too strong a signal on the grid (signal overloading). Excessive excitation voltage will drive the grid positive with respect to the cathode on the positive peaks of the signal. A positive grid draws grid current, which results in distortion of the signal. The

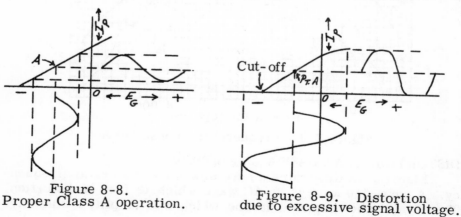

Figure 8-8.
Proper Class A operation.

Figure 8-9.   Distortion
due to excessive signal voltage.

negative peaks of the signal may drive the grid so negative that the tube will cut-off. Cut-off condition results in distortion to the signal. See Figure 8-9.

(2) Improper grid bias. The result of operating the amplifier with too little grid bias is shown in Figure 8-10. Notice that the low bias places the operating point of the tube at the top of the curve instead of the middle of the curve. This causes the positive peaks of the signal voltage to drive the grid into the positive grid voltage region and draw grid current. The resulting distortion is a flattening or clipping of the positive peaks of the plate current output signal.

The result of operating the amplifier with an excessively negative grid bias is shown in Figure 8-11. The negative peaks of the signal drive the tube into cut-off. The resulting distortion is a clipping of the negative peaks of the plate current output signal.

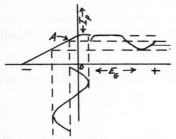

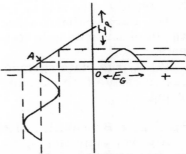

Figure 8-10 Distortion in Class A operation caused by too little bias.

Figure 8-11 Distortion in Class A operation caused by excessive bias.

THE CLASS A POWER AMPLIFIER

A Class A voltage amplifier serves only to amplify weak voltage variations. A voltage amplifier is not required to supply a large power output. The average plate current of a voltage amplifier is therefore comparatively low in value. (A representative value would be about 5 ma). A speaker, however, needs a comparatively large current variation through its voice coil in order to operate properly. The tube which is to drive the speaker must be capable of handling a large amount of power. Such a tube is known as a POWER AMPLIFIER. The plate current of a receiver power amplifier tube may be about 50 ma.

The characteristics of a power amplifier tube are as follows:

(1) A low plate resistance: Since a power tube must be able to handle a relatively high power, it must be capable of conducting

a large plate current. An amplifier tube acts like a resistor. A low plate resistance will enable a large plate current to flow. For example: The plate resistance of the 6BY8 voltage amplifier is about 500,000 ohms and the plate current is approximately 5 ma; whereas the plate resistance of the 6F6 power amplifier is 78,000 ohms and the plate current is about 35 ma.

(2) Large signal handling ability: A large signal on the grid means a large plate current variation. The tube must be capable of handling a large signal without going into cut-off or drawing grid current. This means that the grid will normally operate with a comparatively large bias voltage. The bias voltage for the 6F6 power amplifier is -16 volts, as compared to -1 volt for the 6BY8 voltage amplifier.

(3) A low amplification factor: The amplification factor is directly related to the plate resistance. If the plate resistance is low, the amplification factor will be low. Triode power amplifier tubes usually have a very low amplification factor.

(4) Large cathode structure: The cathode structure must be large in order to be able to supply the large plate current requirements.

(5) Large plate surface structure: The plate surface must be large to enable it to radiate the heat generated by the large plate current flow.

THE CLASS B POWER AMPLIFIER

A power amplifier operated Class A has a comparatively poor operating efficiency. The reason for this is that the tube conducts plate current for the entire cycle of the input signal; this results

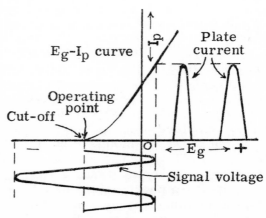

Figure 8-12. Class B operation.

in a continuous dissipation of heat by the plate. Consequently, the maximum power output possibilities of the Class A amplifier are never fully realized.

The modulator stages of radio-telephone transmitters require power audio amplifiers capable of delivering large amounts of power. Class A power amplifiers would not be practical for such an application because of their poor operating efficiency. The Class B power amplifier is therefore used because of its high operating efficiency. A Class B amplifier is biased to cut-off so that plate current is practically zero without a signal. Figure 8-12 illustrates Class B operation on the Eg-Ip curve.

THE CHARACTERISTICS OF THE CLASS B AMPLIFIER

The characteristics of the Class B amplifier are as follows:

(1) Plate current flows only during the positive half of the signal period. The negative half of the signal keeps the tube cut off. (See Figure 8-12). The amplifier operates in a manner similar to that of a rectifier in that it conducts only when the signal is positive.

(2) The amplifier is operated over the entire length of its characteristic curve so that large plate current swings can be obtained. The large plate current swing is necessary if large power output is to be realized.

(3) The efficiency for Class B operation is much higher than that for Class A for two reasons:

(a) Plate current flows for half a cycle, so that the power wasted in heating the plate is very much reduced.

(b) Efficiency of operation increases when a greater portion of the length of the characteristic curve is utilized. The Class B amplifier uses a greater portion of its characteristic curve than a Class A amplifier.

CLASS B PUSH-PULL POWER AMPLIFIER

A Class B amplifier tube, when used alone, will distort the signal because only one half of the input cycle is amplified. Two tubes are therefore necessary, one to amplify the positive half of the input signal and the other to amplify the negative half. The plate output of each tube is combined with the other to form one continuous wave. This system of amplification is called PUSH-PULL AMPLIFICATION.

Figure 8-13 illustrates a basic Class B push-pull amplifier. Its operation is as follows: We will assume that during the positive half of the input cycle, the grid of V1 moves in a positive direction and the grid of V2 goes negative. V1 will conduct current while

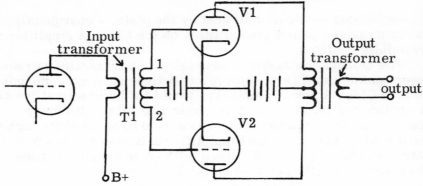

Figure 8-13. Class B push-pull amplifier.

V2 will be cut-off. V1 will therefore amplify the positive half of the signal. During the negative half of the input signal, the grid of V1 goes negative while the grid of V2 goes positive. V1 will cut off and V2 will conduct. V2, therefore, amplifies the negative half of the input signal. The negative plate signal of V2 and positive plate signal of V1 combine in the output to form a complete amplified cycle. This is illustrated in Figure 8-14.

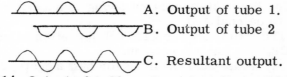

A. Output of tube 1.

B. Output of tube 2

C. Resultant output.

Figure 8-14. Output of a Class B push-pull amplifier.

Push-pull operation has enabled us to utilize the high efficiency of a Class B amplifier, while at the same time, eliminating the distortion inherent in Class B operation.

SECOND HARMONIC DISTORTION

Any distorted waveform may be analyzed and found to consist of a fundamental frequency plus a number of harmonics. Harmonic frequencies are multiples of the fundamental frequency. For example: Let us suppose the original undistorted signal is a 1000 cycle wave. The second harmonic would be 2000 cycles; the third harmonic would be 3000 cycles, etc. This signal, upon being amplified, becomes distorted due to the addition of harmonic frequencies to the original waveform during the process of amplification. In our example, the amplified distorted waveform would be found to consist of the original fundamental frequency of 1000 cycles, plus a second harmonic component of 2000 cycles, plus a third harmonic component of 3000 cycles, etc. The fundamental and the harmonics all add together to give us a resulting distorted waveshape. The second harmonic is usually the most predominant of all the harmonics present. Figure 8-15 illustrates a distorted resultant wave, which is the sum of a fundamental plus a second harmonic component.

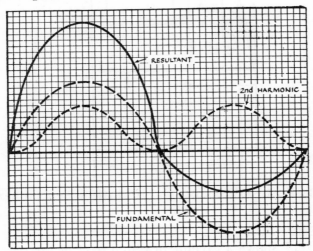

Figure 8-15. Second harmonic distortion.

In an audio amplifier, the distorted signal frequency is converted by the speaker into a distorted sound frequency which sounds unpleasant to the ear. If we could remove this second harmonic from the amplified signal before it reaches the speaker, we would end up with the original undistorted waveform.

Push-pull Class B operation eliminates even-order harmonic distortion. By even order we mean second harmonic, fourth harmonic, etc. Figure 8-16 illustrates the distorted output of two Class A amplifiers connected in push-pull. A Class "A" push-pull amplifier differs from a Class "B" push-pull amplifier in that both tubes in the Class "A" push-pull amplifier conduct current continuously. Both tubes combine their output during both the positive as well as the negative cycles to give us the resulting waveshape. Notice that the two curves combine together, point by point, to produce the resultant undistorted output curve. The second harmonics of V1 and V2 are out of phase with each other across the transformer primary and consequently, cancel each other. By eliminating even (second, fourth, sixth, etc.) harmonic distortion, push-pull operation improves the fidelity of reproduction considerably over that obtainable from one tube (single-ended) operation. A good audio system always uses push-pull amplifiers in its last stage.

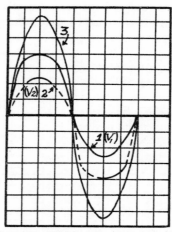

Figure 8-16. Push-pull operation eliminating second harmonic.

INVERSE FEEDBACK

Figure 8-17 shows a circuit in which part of the output signal on the plate of the power tube is fed back to the grid through a resistor and capacitor. Since the plate and grid voltages are out of phase, the feedback signal will be out of phase with the grid signal. If the amount of feedback is correctly adjusted, the harmonics causing distortion may be partially cancelled. Since a portion of the original signal is also being fed back out of phase, the overall gain of the system is reduced. This disadvantage can be overcome by using either high mu tubes or another stage of amplification. As a result of inverse feedback, the distortion is reduced to a great extent.

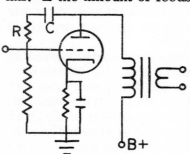

Figure 8-17.
Negative feedback.

Inverse feedback is also known as negative feedback and degenerative feedback.

SOUND

A Class A audio amplifier is used to amplify the small signal output of a microphone. The action of a microphone depends upon certain characteristics of a sound wave. We have, therefore, reached a point in our discussion of amplifiers where a brief resume of the nature of sound becomes necessary.

SOUND is defined as a disturbance in a material medium, caused by the vibration of a body at a certain definite frequency. A sound wave travels through a material medium, such as air or steel, in the form of a compressed wave. This compressed wave travels out from a region of disturbance in exactly the same manner as ripples do when a pebble is dropped into a pool of water. Vibrating objects, such as your vocal cords, cause regions of compressed air followed by rarefied air, to move outward and away from them in the form of concentric spheres. These vibrations or disturbances reach the ear and cause the eardrum to move inward and outward according to the pressure exerted by compressions and rarefactions. The human ear is capable of hearing such disturbances only if they occur within the range from 16 to 16,000 cycles per second. The FREQUENCY RESPONSE of the ear is therefore said to be from 16 to 16,000 cps. This range of frequencies is designated by the term AUDIO FREQUENCIES. Although a frequency vibration of 30,000 cps. will cause the diaphragm in the ear to vibrate, the nerves in the ear are incapable of detecting the vibration.

The frequency range of human hearing varies with the individual. What we hear can depend on our age, physical fitness, sex and musical training.

THE MICROPHONE

An amplifier can only amplify an electrical frequency. Therefore, a sound frequency such as music or voice, must first be converted into an equivalent electrical frequency in order to be amplified.

A microphone is a device which translates or converts sound impulses into varying electrical potentials. These varying electrical potentials constitute the electrical signal and can be impressed between the grid and cathode of the first amplifier tube for purposes of amplification. There are many types of microphones in use today. We shall discuss a few of the common ones.

THE SINGLE-BUTTON CARBON MICROPHONE

Construction: The single-button carbon microphone consists mainly of a diaphragm and a small compartment filled with carbon granules. The compartment is called a "BUTTON". One side of the button is movable and is attached directly to the diaphragm. (See Figure 8-18). A battery and the primary of a transformer are connected in series with the button.

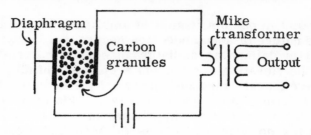

Figure 8-18. Single-button carbon microphone.

Operation: When sound strikes the diaphragm of the microphone, the diaphragm vibrates at the frequency of the sound. This
vibration causes the movable side of the button to move in and out,
thereby causing the packing of the carbon granules to vary. This,
in turn, causes the resistance of the button to vary. The varying
resistance will cause the current in the circuit to vary. The result
is that an audio current, with the same frequency as the original
sound, flows through the primary of the microphone transformer.
Connection: The impedance of the button is about 100 ohms.
A microphone transformer is used to match this low impedance to
the high grid impedance of the first stage.
Frequency response: The single button carbon microphone
responds well to audio frequencies between 250 and 2700 cps. Since
many of the tones of musical instruments lie above 2700 cps, the
carbon microphone is suitable only for speech. The general range
of speech frequencies is below 2700 cps.

OTHER CHARACTERISTICS
(1) The carbon microphone is the most sensitive of all microphones, but is not in much use at the present time. For a given
level of sound input, this microphone will generate a higher signal
voltage than any other microphone.
(2) The carbon microphone is not directional; it picks up
sound impulses equally well from all directions.
(3) Constant current through the granules gives rise to an
annoying background hiss.
(4) Excessive current flowing through the carbon granules or
jarring of the microphone while the current is on, will cause the
microphone to lose its sensitivity.

THE RIBBON OR VELOCITY MICROPHONE
Construction: This microphone is activated by moving air
particles. A thin, corrugated, metallic ribbon is suspended between the poles of a strong permanent magnet.
Operation: Sound energy strikes the ribbon and causes it to

move back and forth, thereby cutting the magnetic field. The cut-ting action induces an emf. in the ribbon; this emf. is the audio signal. The emf. frequency is determined by the frequency of the sound wave which strikes the ribbon. The impedance of the short piece of ribbon may be as low as 0.5 ohm. A matching transform-er is employed to match the low output impedance of the ribbon microphone to the high grid input impedance.

Frequency Response: The frequency response is fairly flat from 30 to 12,000 cps. This wide frequency range is satisfactory for the transmission of music as well as sound.

Other Characteristics: (1) To prevent booming effect, the microphone should be placed at least fourteen inches away from the source of sound.

(2) This microphone is bi-directional; maximum pick-up oc-curs at the front and back of the head of the microphone.

(3) It is desirable as a broadcast microphone because of its flat frequency response.

THE CRYSTAL MICROPHONE

Construction: The active element in a crystal microphone is a crystalline material, usually Rochelle salts. Other crystals that may be used are quartz and tourmaline. There are two types of crystal microphones:

(1) Diaphragm type in which a thin diaphragm is rigidly fixed to one of the major faces of the crystal.

(2) Sound cell type in which a series of crystals are excited by sound pressure directly, without the use of a diaphragm. We shall examine the sound cell type of crystal microphone, as it is the most commonly used of the two types of crystal microphones.

Operation: Certain crystals, like Rochelle salts, develop a potential difference between two surfaces when a mechanical pres-sure is applied to their opposite surfaces. Sound pressure applied to a crystal surface will develop a varying electrical potential across the opposite surface at the frequency of the sound wave. In this manner, sound energy is converted into electrical energy. The varying potential that is developed is applied to the grid cir-cuit of an amplifier for further amplification.

Connection: The crystal microphone is about the simplest microphone to connect. It requires no battery, since it generates its own potential. The crystal microphone requires no transform-er because it has a high impedance (over one megohm) and is, therefore, a good match to the high impedance of the grid circuit.

Frequency Response: The frequency response of the crystal microphone is from 50 to 8000 cps. This is satisfactory for speech reproduction, but not quite satisfactory for high fidelity music.

Other Characteristics: (1) A crystal microphone should be handled with care because any shock is likely to impair its operation.

(2) It should not be exposed to excessive temperature and humidity changes.

(3) It is used in portable, mobile and fixed station equipment.

(4) A single sound cell type of crystal microphone is not directional: multiple cell types can be designed for directional use.

THE REPRODUCER

The process of amplification consists of three individual steps:

(1) Conversion of sound energy to electrical energy (by the microphone).

(2) Amplification of the converted electrical energy.

(3) Conversion of the amplified electrical energy back into sound energy.

This last step is accomplished by means of a REPRODUCER. Of the many types of reproducers in use today, we will study the headphones (earphones) and the permanent magnet (PM) speaker.

THE RADIO HEADPHONE

The radio headphone or telephone receiver is the simplest type of reproducer. It consists basically of an iron core electromagnet and a metal diaphragm. This is illustrated in Figure 8-19. The diaphragm is separated from the electromagnet by a few thousandths of an inch.

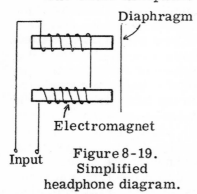

Figure 8-19.
Simplified
headphone diagram.

Audio currents are sent through the coils of the electromagnet. This causes the field of the coils to alternately weaken and strengthen. The diaphragm vibrates in accordance with this varying field and sets the surrounding air into motion. This air motion constitutes the sound waves which travel to the ear of the listener.

The impedance of most electromagnetic headphones is about 2000 ohms. This value is high enough for the headphones to be used directly as a plate load for a voltage amplifier triode without the need of a matching transformer.

THE PERMANENT MAGNET SPEAKER

The most commonly used type of speaker today is the permanent magnet type and is commonly referred to as a PM speaker. The speaker consists of three basic parts: a powerful magnet, a coil of fine wire known as a voice coil and a cone made of paper or fibre.

The permanent magnet is ordinarily an Alnico type, so-called since it consists of a combination of aluminum, nickel and cobalt. The voice coil consists of a number of turns of wire wound on a light-weight form and mounted between the poles of the magnet. The ends of the voice coil are connected to the secondary winding of the audio output transformer. The voice-coil becomes an electromagnet when audio currents flow through it.   The forces of magnetic attraction and repulsion between the voice coil and the Alnico magnet cause the voice coil to move back and forth. As it does so, it moves the cone which is attached to it. The movement of the cone causes alternate compressions and rarefactions of the air molecules surrounding the cone. The result is the sensation we know as sound.

THE TRANSISTOR AS AN AUDIO AMPLIFIER

Transistors can be operated Class A, Class B or Class C in the same manner as tubes can. As in tube circuits, the class of operation in transistor amplifiers depends upon the amount of bias.

Figure 8-20 illustrates a single-ended transistor audio amplifier whose output load is a speaker. The driver stage delivers the audio signal to the base of the P-N-P output transistor. Resistance-capacitance coupling is used, and if you will compare this circuit with that of Figure 8-5, you will see a number of resemblances. The only difference is in the values of the components used. For instance, the coupling capacitor, C1, has a much larger amount of capacitance than the one used in the tube circuit.

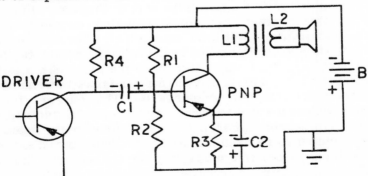

Figure 8-20. A single-ended transistor audio amplifier.

A single 4-1/2 volt battery is used to supply both forward and reverse bias. If you will examine R1 and R2, you will see that they are in series. Further examination reveals that this series combination is shunted across the 4-1/2 volt battery. As a result, the top end of R1 is negative and the bottom end is positive. This means that the point at which R1 and R2 join (at the base) is minus with respect to ground. But ground is connected to the emitter through the low resistance of R3. Thus, we have made the base negative with respect to the emitter, a necessary condition of reverse bias for this P-N-P transistor. The collector is also negative with respect to the emitter. The collector gets its voltage from the 4-1/2 volt battery through the primary (L1) of the audio output transformer.

The audio signal that is delivered to the base of the output transistor by C1 appears across R2. This varies the voltage across R2; hence, the amount of forward bias is varied. The effect is similar to that of an audio signal varying the bias between grid and cathode of a tube. As a result, the collector current of the transistor also varies. This varying current, at an audio rate, passes through the primary of L1 and induces a similarly varying voltage across the secondary winding of the output transformer (L2).

Since the collector is negative and the emitter is positive, current flows through the P-N-P transistor from the collector to the emitter. This may seem surprising since the collector is often compared to the plate of a tube and the emitter is compared to the cathode. Unlike tubes, though, in transistors, current can flow from emitter to collector, or from collector to emitter. The N-P-N transistor more nearly resembles the tube since the current flow in the N-P-N type is from emitter to collector.

Resistor R3 and capacitor C2 resemble the cathode resistor and bypass capacitor of a tube. However, in this case, they do not supply bias; they protect the transistor against excessive current flow. They do so in the following manner:

Transistor current flows down through R3, making the top end of R3 negative and the bottom end of R3 positive. This is in opposition to the forward bias. As the forward bias increases, current flow through the transistor increases. This current flow tends to raise the temperature of the transistor, reducing its resistance. As a consequence, more current passes through the transistor, raising its temperature even higher. A condition known as thermal runaway can result and this will cause the transistor to burn out.

With R3 in the circuit however, the voltage developed across R3 opposes the forward bias. When current through the transistor increases, so does the voltage drop across R3, and thus we get a still greater voltage opposing the forward bias. This keeps the current from rising. Since the voltage across R3 is due to the varying current through the transistor, we keep the voltage as constant as possible by putting a large value electrolytic capacitor (C2) across R3. If C2 is omitted, the effect is similar to negative feedback and as a result, the gain of the transistor amplifier will decrease.

TYPES OF COUPLING

Although we have shown an R-C amplifier, transistor amplifiers are normally transformer coupled. The reason for this is that it is easy for an audio transformer to match the output and input impedances of transistors. Audio transformers were used in early radio sets when triodes were popular, but gave way to R-C coupling when tetrodes and pentodes were introduced. Tetrodes and pentodes have a very high plate impedance and it is difficult to match this impedance with an audio transformer.

THE HEAT SINK

Power transistors used in the audio output stages of amplifiers often carry a very heavy current and so tend to get quite hot. To dissipate the heat, the transistors are mounted on large metal surfaces which are ribbed or corrugated to supply as large a radiating surface as possible. Some of these radiators, known as heat sinks, have metal fins.

THERMISTORS

One of the problems encountered with transistors, but which does not appear with tubes, is stability of operation. The difficulty is that the transistor is a temperature sensitive device. As the temperature goes up, the current flowing between the emitter and collector (or between collector and emitter) increases. Various methods are used to stabilize transistors and the emitter resistor mentioned in connection with Figure 8-20 is just one technique.

Another technique is to use a thermistor, a component whose resistance varies inversely with temperature. This means that as the temperature goes up, the resistance of the thermistor goes down, and vice versa. Thermistors come in a large variety of shapes, such as washers, rods or discs. They are made of manganese, nickel oxide and cobalt oxide.

Figure 8-21 shows a transistor circuit using a thermistor. The thermistor symbol is shown as a variable resistor (which it really is). The thermistor is shunted across R2. Since R2 is connected between the base and emitter (the emitter resistor has

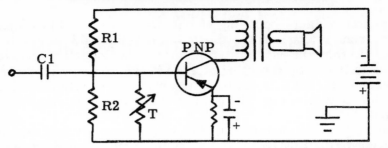

Figure 8-21. A transistor circuit using a thermistor.

a very low value), the voltage across R2 determines the forward bias. The thermistor, shunted across R2, is mounted close to the transistor. If the temperature of the transistor should rise, the resistance of the thermistor will decrease. But this, in turn, will decrease the resistance between the base and emitter, thus decreasing the amount of forward bias. The decrease in forward bias will reduce the amount of current flowing between collector and emitter.

VARISTORS

The varistor is still another device that is used to prevent thermal current runaway in transistors. Varistors are generally made of a semiconductor material, such as silicon carbide. While it is somewhat similar to a copper oxide or selenium rectifier, the varistor permits current to flow equally well in both directions.

A characteristic of varistors is that their resistance drops very rapidly as the voltage across them goes up. Varistors, manufactured in the form of thin rods or wide discs, are used in power supplies for voltage regulation purposes.

CHAPTER 9

INTRODUCTION TO TRANSMISSION AND RECEPTION

INTRODUCTION

The first eight chapters of this book were devoted to a study of vacuum tubes and transistors, fundamental radio theory and basic circuits. These chapters gave us the background material for our discussion of transmitters and receivers. However, before we go into a detailed study of actual transmitter and receiver circuits, we will take a bird's eye view of a complete communications system. Instead of drawing out the individual circuits, we will draw a series of boxes, each box representing a stage. (A stage is a tube or transistor with its associated parts). The function of each stage will be printed inside the box. Such a diagram is known as a block diagram. Figure 9-1 illustrates a block diagram of a radio-telephone transmitter and Figure 9-2 illustrates the block diagram of a receiver.

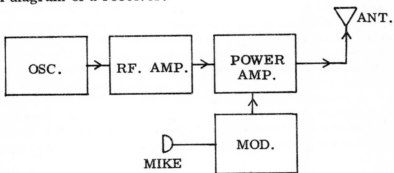

Figure 9-1.   The radio transmitter.

THE TRANSMITTER

In the early development of radio, it was found that the magnetic fields resulting from high-frequency currents were able to travel long distances through space. One of the primary functions of the transmitter is to develop this high frequency signal. This is accomplished in the OSCILLATOR stage. The oscillator stage is actually the heart of the transmitter.

The output of the oscillator is fed to the RADIO-FREQUENCY AMPLIFIER. The function of the radio-frequency amplifier is to amplify the output of the oscillator.

The output of the RF amplifier is then fed to the RF POWER AMPLIFIER. The RF power amplifier amplifies the RF in terms of power. The power amplifier then supplies the antenna with this amplified RF power.

Up to this point, we have only discussed the generation and transmission of a radio frequency wave that does not contain any speech. The three stages, discussed so far, can transmit only code. If we desire to transmit speech, we must add a microphone and one or more stages.

We have already studied the microphone in detail. Its function is to convert sound energy into electrical energy. The output of the microphone is applied to the modulator, which is simply an audio amplifier. The modulator serves two functions: (1) It amplifies the weak audio output of the microphone and (2) It superimposes the audio on to the radio frequency energy that is present at the power amplifier stage. This process is called modulation. The audio waves are not capable of traveling through space and therefore, must be combined with an RF wave in order to be transmitted. Thus, the RF acts as the "carrier" for the audio; the RF carries the audio from the transmitter to the receiver. The combined audio-RF output of the power amplifier is fed to the antenna where it is radiated out into space in the form of electromagnetic waves.

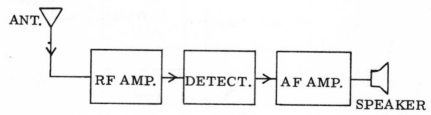

Figure 9-2. The receiver.

THE RECEIVER

At the receiving end of the communications system, the electromagnetic waves induce small signal voltages into the receiving antenna. These signal voltages are quite weak because the electromagnetic waves have traveled some distance before striking the receiving antenna. The signal voltages must therefore be amplified; this is the function of the RF amplifier, the first stage in the receiver. The output of this stage is applied to the detector. Just as the oscillator is the heart of the transmitter, the detector is the heart of the receiver. The detector stage separates the audio from he RF carrier. The carrier has now served its purpose in bringing the audio to the receiver. All that we are actually interested n is the audio. The audio output of the detector is then fed to an audio amplifier stage to be amplified. The amplified audio is applied to a speaker which converts the audio electrical variations back into the original sound that energized the microphone of the ransmitter.

Thus, we have briefly described a modern communications system. The remaining chapters will go into the details of each stage of the communications system.

CHAPTER 10

OSCILLATORS

INTRODUCTION TO OSCILLATORS
Simply speaking, a vacuum tube oscillator is an electronic
alternating current generator. It is a device used to generate an
alternating current of any desired frequency. All transmitters and
practically all receivers, use a vacuum tube or transistor oscillator. Vacuum tube or transistor oscillators are also employed
in various types of instruments used for testing and adjusting radio
equipment. Because oscillators find so many applications, various
types of oscillator circuits have been developed. However, the
operation of the different types of oscillators is fundamentally the
same.

THE OSCILLATING TUNED CIRCUIT
The heart of an oscillator is a TUNED CIRCUIT which consists
of a coil and capacitor in parallel. In order to understand how a
complete oscillator works, it is first necessary to see how a simple tuned circuit can produce alternating current oscillations. An
elementary oscillatory circuit is shown in Figure 10-1. When the
switch, "S", is thrown to the left, the capacitor, "C", is placed
across the battery. The coil, "L", is out of the circuit. "C" will

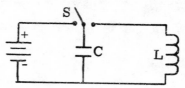

Figure 10-1. An elementary oscillatory circuit.

charge up to the voltage of the battery. The upper plate of "C"
will become positive and the lower plate will become negative. A
certain amount of electrical energy is, therefore, stored on the
plates of the capacitor by the charging process. If the switch is
then thrown to the right, the capacitor will discharge through the
coil "L". The electrons will flow from the lower plate of "C",
through the coil and back to the upper plate of "C". The flow of
electrons will build up a magnetic field around "L". The energy
which was stored in the capacitor has now been transferred to the
130

magnetic field surrounding the coil. When "C" is discharged completely, the flow of electrons through "L" tends to cease, causing
the magnetic field to start collapsing. The collapsing magnetic
field induces a voltage of such a polarity across "L" that it maintains the flow of electrons to the upper plate of the capacitor. This
occurs because the magnetic field acts to prevent a change in the
flow of current (Lenz's Law). The flow of electrons to the upper
plate continues until the magnetic field has completely collapsed.
The capacitor now becomes charged with its top plate negative and
its bottom plate positive. The energy which was in the magnetic
field has now been transferred to the capacitor in the form of a
stored charge. The capacitor is now charged in the opposite polarity to its original charge. The capacitor again discharges
through "L" and the entire action as outlined above repeats itself.
Thus we can see that the energy or current OSCILLATES back and
forth between the coil and the capacitor, alternately charging "C"
first in one direction and then in the other. This alternating current will produce an alternating voltage across the tuned circuit.
The frequency of this AC voltage is determined by the values of
"L" and "C".

THE DAMPED AND UNDAMPED WAVE
     If there were no resistance in either the coil or the capacitor,
there would be no energy loss. The oscillations would therefore
continue forever at a constant amplitude. A graph, illustrating
this condition is shown in Figure 10-2A. The wave is called an

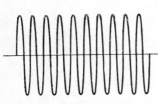
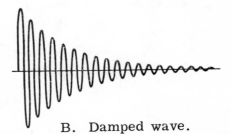

A. Undamped wave.   B. Damped wave.

Figure 10-2. Oscillations.

UNDAMPED WAVE (continuous oscillations). Some resistance is
always present in radio components, especially in a coil. This
resistance causes some of the energy which oscillates back and
forth in the tuned circuit, to be transformed into heat. The heat,
of course, is a loss of energy. Therefore, with each succeeding

cycle, the amplitude of the oscillating voltage decreases until all of the energy has been dissipated in the form of heat. Fig. 10-2B illustrates the diminishing oscillations. We call this a DAMPED WAVE.

CONDITION FOR OSCILLATION

In radio, it is necessary that the tuned circuit oscillations continue at a constant amplitude – just like the undamped wave of Figure 10-2A. If we want the oscillations to continue, we must make up for the resistance losses which occur in the L-C circuit. We must somehow inject electrical energy back into the L-C circuit to sustain the oscillations. Where is this energy to come from and how do we inject it properly into the L-C circuit? To answer these questions, we can compare the oscillations of energy in the tuned circuit to a child on a swing. In order that the child keep swinging to a constant height, it is necessary that someone give the swing a little push each time the child reaches the top of his swing. In other words, energy must be added to the swing at the right time to overcome the friction in the hinges, otherwise the swing will gradually come to rest, just like the damped wave oscillations. In radio, the answer to the question of how to maintain oscillation lies in the use of the amplifying ability of the electron tube.

When a vacuum tube is hooked up to a power supply, the AC energy developed in the plate circuit is much greater than that applied to the grid circuit; this is due to the tube's amplification. If the oscillating circuit of Figure 10-1 were to be connected to the grid circuit of a vacuum tube, an amplified version of the oscillating voltage would appear in the plate circuit. If we could somehow continuously feed back some energy from the plate circuit to the grid circuit to compensate for the resistance losses in the L-C

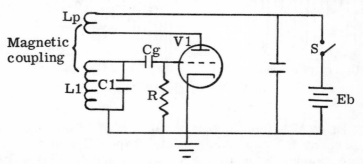

Figure 10-3. Tickler-coil oscillator or Armstrong oscillator.

grid circuit, oscillations could continue like the undamped wave of Figure 10-2A. A simple method of doing this is shown in Figure 10-3. L1 and C1 represent the tuned circuit, sometimes called the TANK CIRCUIT. V1 is the triode amplifier tube. Lp is a coil of wire wound on the same form and placed next to L1. Since Lp is in the plate circuit, it is easy to see that some of the amplified energy from the plate circuit is fed back to the grid circuit through the magnetic coupling between the two coils. If this energy can overcome the losses in the tank circuit, oscillations will be maintained.

The entire circuit of Figure 10-3 is called a vacuum tube oscillator. This particular oscillator has found wide practical use, especially in receivers. It is known by the names of the TUNED GRID OSCILLATOR, TICKLER COIL OSCILLATOR, or the ARMSTRONG OSCILLATOR. We shall now discuss, in more detail, the operation of this vacuum tube oscillator.

OPERATION OF A VACUUM TUBE OSCILLATOR

As soon as the switch "S" is turned on, a surge of plate current flows through the plate coil, Lp. This surging current builds up an expanding magnetic field around Lp. The expanding field cuts through L1 and induces an emf. in it. The induced emf. across the coil will now charge the capacitor of the tuned circuit. The capacitor then discharges through L1 and the oscillatory action, previously described, begins. The losses in the tank circuit are overcome by a feed-back of energy from the plate circuit to the grid circuit by means of magnetic coupling between Lp and L1. In this manner, the oscillations of the tuned circuit are maintained at a constant amplitude.

Lp, called the TICKLER COIL or FEEDBACK COIL, must be wound in such a direction so that an expanding field about it induces a voltage in L1, which causes the grid to go positive. A positive grid will cause the plate current and the field around Lp to further increase and induce energy back into L1. The process of transferring energy from Lp of the plate circuit to L1 of the grid circuit is called INDUCTIVE FEEDBACK or MAGNETIC FEEDBACK. Since the energy fed back to the tuned circuit is sufficient to make up for the energy lost in the resistance of the tank circuit, the oscillations will continue and will not die down. If the tickler coil is wound in such a direction as to make the grid negative, the oscillator will NOT start oscillating at all.

From the above explanation, we realize that the vacuum tube itself does not oscillate. The oscillations actually take place in the tuned circuit. The vacuum tube simply functions as an electrical valve which automatically controls the release of energy back into the tuned circuit. The feedback energy overcomes losses and maintains oscillations.

The above explanation of the operation of an oscillator is basic to all oscillator circuits that will be covered in this chapter.

GRID-LEAK BIAS

Efficient operation of an RF oscillator requires that it have a high negative bias. There are several ways of obtaining this large bias. One way is by means of a battery; another is by means of a negative voltage power supply. However, in the case of an oscillator, the only practical way of obtaining this high negative bias is by means of a resistor and capacitor connected in the grid circuit, as shown in Figure 10-3. This type of bias is called GRID-LEAK BIAS. Grid-leak bias is used in all oscillators. A simple explanation of grid-leak bias is as follows:

When the peaks of the oscillations in the tank circuit of Figure 10-3 drive the grid positive with respect to the cathode, grid current, Ig, flows in the grid circuit. A positive grid attracts electrons, as does a positive plate. The grid current flow charges capacitor Cg in the manner shown in Figure 10-4A. During the remainder of the cycle, the grid does not conduct and the capacitor discharges through R, as shown in Figure 10-4B. The current flows through R in a direction that causes the top or grid side of R to become negative with respect to the bottom or cathode side.

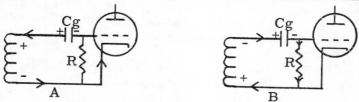

Figure 10-4. Grid-leak bias.

This voltage is the grid-leak bias voltage, which makes the control grid negative with respect to the cathode. Because of the heavy grid-leak bias, plate current flows only during the positive peaks of the oscillations. Since the plate current flows for only a small part of a cycle, the average power wasted inside the tube is reduced, and the efficiency of the oscillator is increased. The fact that the plate current does not flow continuously does not hinder oscillations, because it is only necessary to feed back small pulses of energy in every cycle to sustain the oscillations.

FREQUENCY OF OSCILLATION

The larger the value of the inductance in the tuned circuit, the longer it will take for the capacitor to discharge through the inductance. Likewise, the larger the capacitance, the longer it will take the capacitor to charge or discharge. Since the time of a cycle of oscillation depends upon the charge and discharge time, it can be seen that the frequency of the oscillator goes down as the inductance or capacitance is increased. On the other hand, the frequency goes up if the inductance or capacitance is made smaller. The formula for the frequency of an oscillator is:

$$(10\text{-}1) \quad F = \frac{1}{2\pi\sqrt{LC}}$$

Where: F is the frequency in cycles
L is the tank inductance in henries
C is the tank capacitance in farads.

In order to vary the frequency of the oscillator, it is necessary to vary the value of the inductance or the capacitance. In most receivers and transmitters, a variable capacitor is used in the tank circuit to vary the frequency of the oscillator.

THE HARTLEY OSCILLATOR

A popular oscillator that is frequently used in electronics circuits is the HARTLEY OSCILLATOR. Its principle of operation is very similar to that of the Armstrong oscillator. Instead of having two separate plate and grid coils, the Hartley oscillator has a single coil which is tapped. The Hartley oscillator can always be recognized by its tapped coil (see Figure 10-5). One part of the coil (Lp), is in the plate circuit and the other part (Lg), is in the grid circuit. Capacitor C is across the entire coil. The resonant frequency of this oscillator is determined by C and Lg and Lp in series. You will recall that in the Armstrong oscillator energy is fed back by the inductive coupling between the tickler coil and the grid coil. The feedback in the Hartley oscillator is also due to inductive coupling (between Lp and Lg). The tickler coil may be represented by Lp. The amount of feedback can be controlled by varying the position of the tap on the coil. The theory of operation of the Hartley oscillator is exactly the same as the Armstrong oscillator.

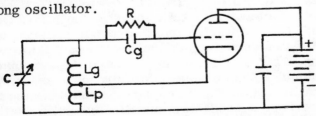

Figure 10-5. Series-fed Hartley oscillator.

FREQUENCY STABILITY OF OSCILLATORS

If an oscillator remains in operation continuously, it will be found that the frequency of the oscillator drifts with time. For example, when an oscillator is first turned on, it may start to oscillate at a frequency of 1000 kc. After the oscillator warms up, the frequency may drift either above or below 1000 kc. Frequency drift is highly undesirable in a broadcast transmitter since it would cause fading of the signal at the receiver end. Similarly, oscillators in test equipment must have a minimum of frequency drift if the equipment is to serve any useful purpose. The causes of oscillator drift and its prevention are subjects of importance to all radio technicians.

Oscillator frequency drift may be caused by the following factors:

(1) Improper design of the oscillator circuit
    a. choosing the wrong combination of L and C for the tank circuit.
(2) Poor voltage regulation of the oscillator power supply
    a. changes in B+ voltage will cause voltage variations at the screen and plate. This will vary the oscillator frequency. A well-regulated oscillator power supply is therefore necessary for good frequency stability.
(3) Changes in plate resistance and interelectrode capacitance of a tube will cause the frequency to vary.
(4) Changes in temperature will cause the inductance and capacitance of the tank circuit to vary. A physical change in either L or C will change the oscillating frequency.
(5) Changes in loading of the oscillator
    a. If the output of the oscillator is fed directly into a varying load, the frequency of the oscillator will be affected. The oscillator must be isolated from the varying load in order to maintain good frequency stability.

CRYSTAL-CONTROLLED OSCILLATORS

The most stable of all oscillators is the CRYSTAL-CONTROLLED OSCILLATOR. The most important difference between the oscillators studied so far and the crystal oscillator is that the oscillator tuned circuit, consisting of L and C, is replaced by a crystal substance. This crystal is usually made out of quartz, a mineral found in the earth. The quartz crystal has the following peculiar property: If a mechanical vibration is applied to the quartz crystal, an electrical voltage will be developed across its surfaces.

On the other hand, if we apply an alternating voltage to the surfaces of the quartz crystal, it will vibrate mechanically. This property of quartz is known as the PIEZO-ELECTRIC EFFECT.

If we momentarily apply an AC voltage to two parallel surfaces of the crystal, it will start to vibrate mechanically. This mechanical vibration will, in turn, generate an AC voltage. This AC voltage will again cause the crystal to vibrate, etc. etc. This process will continue until all of the electrical energy which was injected into the crystal is used up. The crystal, from an electrical viewpoint, acts in the same manner as a tuned circuit. If energy is injected into a crystal, an electrical oscillation is generated across the crystal surface, which continues until all of the energy has been used up. Since the vibrating crystal is similar to a tuned circuit, it can be placed in the grid circuit of an oscillator in place of the actual tuned grid circuit. A schematic of a triode crystal oscillator is shown in Figure 10-6. Energy from the plate tuned circuit is fed back to the grid circuit, through the grid-plate capacitance of the tube. The energy that is fed back to the grid circuit keeps the crystal oscillating. The oscillations occur at the resonant frequency of the crystal, and the plate circuit is tuned approximately to this frequency. The resonant frequency of a crystal is mainly determined by its thickness.

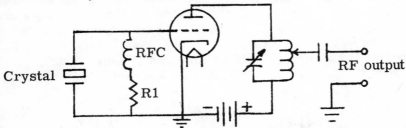

Figure 10-6. Crystal-controlled oscillator.

The strength of the crystal's vibrations depends upon the voltage being fed back to the crystal. If the feedback is too great, the vibrations may become strong enough to crack or shatter the crystal. The use of a tetrode or pentode overcomes this difficulty because the screen grid reduces the feedback. However, the little energy that does get back is sufficient to sustain the crystal's oscillations.

Tetrodes and pentodes are also more sensitive than triodes and require less grid voltage for satisfactory oscillator operation. The purpose of the RF choke in Figure 10-6 is to make sure that the feed-back energy gets to the crystal and is not by-passed to ground through R1.

CHAPTER 11

TRANSMITTERS

Radio transmitters are divided into two types. One is the CONTINUOUS-WAVE type of transmitter; the other is the MODU-LATED type of transmitter. The continuous-wave type is used to transmit code signals, while the modulated type sends out sound such as speech, music, etc. We will first study the continuous-wave transmitter.

CONTINUOUS WAVES

Continuous waves, abbreviated CW, are radio waves of constant amplitude. In the CW transmitter, continuous waves are radiated into space by simply coupling the output of a vacuum tube or transistor power oscillator to a suitable antenna system. The International Morse Code is used to convey intelligence by CW communication. In the Morse code, various combinations of dots and dashes represent the letters of the alphabet. In order to transmit code, the CW transmission must be interrupted in a dot and dash sequence. This type of emission is actually an RF wave, broken up into sections. An oscillator is made to stop and start oscillating by means of a telegraph key. By allowing the oscillator to operate for longer or shorter amounts of time, we can produce dots and dashes. Figure 11-1 shows the output of an oscillator for the letter "D" (dash-dot-dot).

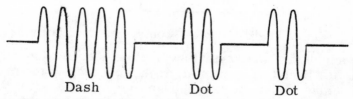

Dash   Dot   Dot

Figure 11-1. Keyed output of an oscillator
for the letter "D" (dash-dot-dot).

ONE-TUBE TRANSMITTER

In early type radio transmitters, the oscillator was directly coupled to the antenna system. In order to increase the power output of this type of transmitter, it was necessary to use a larger tube or to increase the operating voltages. There is a limit, however, to the amount of power that one can get from a one-tube transmitter. The power output of an oscillator depends upon RF currents in the oscillator circuit. Since these currents are relatively weak, very little power can be delivered to the antenna. The radiated wave, therefore, will also be weak. Another defect of the simple oscillator type of transmitter is its poor frequency stability. Figure 11-2 shows a one-tube transmitter. Capacitor CA represents the antenna capacitance to ground. This will vary as the antenna swings in the wind. This varying antenna capacitance will be coupled back to the tank circuit and will cause the oscillator frequency to vary. The disadvantage of poor frequency stability can be overcome to a great extent by the use of an RF amplifier stage which serves to isolate the antenna from the oscillator. Changes in antenna capacitance will therefore not be reflected into the oscillator tank circuit. At the same time, the RF amplifier amplifies the output of the oscillator and feeds a more powerful signal into the antenna.

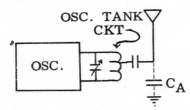

Figure 11-2.   One-tube transmitter.

MASTER-OSCILLATOR POWER-AMPLIFIER

A transmitter consisting of an oscillator and an amplifier (or a series of amplifiers) is called a MASTER-OSCILLATOR POWER-AMPLIFIER, MOPA for short. Such a transmitter is shown in Figure 11-3. The output of the oscillator is amplified by V2. Capacitor C1 prevents the high DC voltage on the plate of V1 from being applied to the grid of V2. At the same time, it allows the RF energy to get through to the grid of V2. The RF choke, L1, prevents the RF energy from flowing to ground through R1. This is because an RF choke opposes the flow of RF currents.

The master-oscillator power-amplifier type of transmitter has a decided advantage over the simple oscillator transmitter in that the frequency stability is greatly improved. High frequency stability is obtained in this system because the oscillator is not coupled directly to the antenna. The oscillator is therefore unaffected by any change in the antenna-to-ground capacitance. Changes in antenna-to-ground capacitance will merely react upon the RF power amplifier circuit, resulting in a slight decrease in the ra-

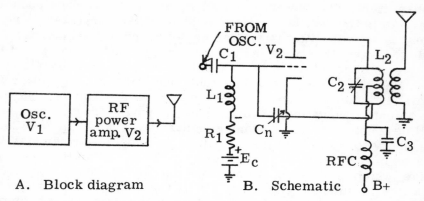

A. Block diagram   B. Schematic

Figure 11-3. Master-oscillator, power-amplifier transmitter.

diated power output. The amplifier of Figure 11-3 may feed the antenna directly, or it may be the first of a series of RF amplifiers, the last of which feeds into an antenna system.

HIGH EFFICIENCY CLASS C RF AMPLIFIER

In a previous chapter, we studied the biasing methods for audio amplifiers. You will recall that AF amplifiers were operated as Class A or Class B amplifiers because we were interested in obtaining good fidelity of reproduction. The Class A amplifier sacrifices efficiency for excellent fidelity. In the case of an RF amplifier, we are not interested in fidelity since we are not amplifying an audio signal. We are interested in efficiency of operation. An RF amplifier operates most efficiently in a transmitter as a Class C amplifier. In order to operate the tube as a Class C amplifier, the bias must be between one and one-half to four times the bias value necessary for cut-off. This condition is shown graphically in Figure 11-4. You will notice that with a pure sine wave applied to the grid, the plate current consists of small pulses which certainly do not resemble the input sine wave. Since the plate current wave does not resemble the grid signal, the fidelity of a Class C amplifier is poor. The important point to notice is that the plate current flows for only a fraction of the period of the input signal. Compare this to a Class A amplifier where the plate current flows continuously. Obviously, more power is wasted in plate dissipation in a Class A amplifier than in a Class C amplifier. Since the plate dissipation is decreased in the Class C amplifier, the useful power output is increased. The efficiency of a Class C amplifier is therefore excellent. It is approximately 70%

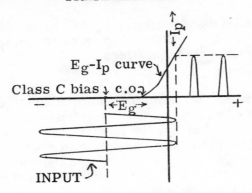

Figure 11-4.   Class "C" bias operation.

efficient.

The question that always arises at this point is: Of what good are the plate current pulses if we are interested in obtaining an amplified version of the sine wave input? The answer lies in the ability of the plate tank circuit to reproduce a relatively pure sine wave from pulses of energy which are applied to it every cycle. This principle was fully discussed in the last chapter.

GRID-LEAK BIAS

It was mentioned above that a Class C amplifier requires a bias of from one and one-half to four times the value of cut-off bias. There are several methods of obtaining Class C bias. The first method that we shall discuss is known as GRID-LEAK BIAS. You will recall that grid-leak bias is used in the self-biased os-cillator. Figure 11-3 shows the RF amplifier, V2, employing grid-leak bias. R1 is the bias resistor and C1 is the bias capacitor. Before the signal from the previous stage is applied to the grid of the amplifier tube, the bias on the grid is zero. However, when a signal is applied, a grid bias voltage develops across R1. Let us review once again how this comes about: On the positive half of the incoming signal, the grid is driven positive with respect to the cathode. This causes a flow of grid current, which charges capacitor C1. On the negative half of the signal, the capacitor dis-charges through R1. The discharge current that flows through R1 develops a DC voltage across R1. Capacitor C1, which is effec-tively in parallel with R1, tends to keep this voltage constant. Since the current enters R1 at the top (the grid side), the top part of the resistor is negative with respect to the bottom part. There-fore, the grid is negatively biased with respect to the cathode.

Among other factors, the amount of grid-leak bias that is de-veloped depends upon the strength of the signal. This may sometimes be a serious disadvantage. If, for some reason, the signal or excitation is lost, the bias will disappear and the plate current may rise to excessively high values.

FIXED BIAS

Another method of obtaining bias for Class C amplifiers is through the use of a battery. The negative terminal of the battery is connected to the grid and the positive terminal is connected to the cathode. An RF by-pass capacitor is usually shunted across the battery to complete the RF path around the battery. The amount of battery voltage to be used for a particular tube can be found by consulting a transmitting tube manual.

COMBINATION GRID-LEAK, CATHODE BIAS

A third method of obtaining bias is shown in Fig. 11-5. This method is a combination of grid-leak and cathode bias. R1 provides most of the bias voltage. R2 is placed in the circuit to act

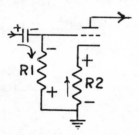

Figure 11-5.

as a protective bias in case the input signal to the stage should fail. Upon loss of grid-leak bias, the increased plate current will flow through R2, developing a heavy bias voltage, which will, in turn, limit the plate current to a safe value. R2 will not cause any appreciable loss of plate voltage, since its value is small. It will simply serve to bias the tube should the grid-leak bias disappear.

NEUTRALIZATION

Examine the RF amplifier of Figure 11-6. Note that the tank circuit L2C2 is not only the plate tank circuit of the oscillator, but can also be considered as the grid tank circuit of the RF amplifier. The portion of the schematic of Figure 11-6 inside the dotted line is exactly the same as a type of oscillator called the tuned-plate, tuned-grid oscillator. This portion of the circuit will therefore oscillate unless certain precautions are taken. An oscillating RF amplifier is very undesirable. An amplifier is supposed to amplify and not to oscillate.

There are two general methods of preventing an RF amplifier from oscillating. One is to use a tetrode or pentode instead of a triode. As you have previously learned, the addition of a screen grid reduces the grid-plate capacitance. It would therefore be very difficult for a tetrode or pentode to oscillate, since there

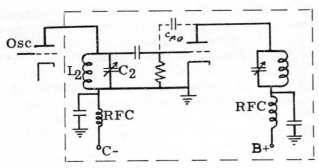

Figure 11-6. Oscillatory circuit in an unneutralized RF amplifier.

would be insufficient feedback through the grid-plate capacitance. Most high powered RF amplifying tubes, however, are triodes and therefore, we have the problem of preventing oscillations from taking place. This problem can be solved by the addition of special neutralizing capacitors. These neutralizing capacitors are placed in the circuit in such a way that they cancel the effect of the grid-plate capacitance and thereby prevent oscillation.

THE MODULATED TRANSMITTER

Communication by means of CW (code) transmission is known as RADIOTELEGRAPHY. The disadvantage of radiotelegraphy is that the radio operator must know code. In order for operators who are not familiar with code to be able to send and receive messages directly, the transmission of speech is necessary. The transmission of audio (speech) by means of radio communication is known as RADIOTELEPHONY.

A radiotelephone transmitter consists of a CW transmitter (minus the telegraph key) plus an audio frequency amplifier system. The audio frequency system amplifies the audio signals and superimposes them on the RF signal that is generated by the RF oscillator. THE PROCESS OF SUPERIMPOSING THE AUDIO ON THE RF IS KNOWN AS MODULATION. The RF signal is called a CARRIER since it "carries" the audio through space to the receiving antenna.

AMPLITUDE MODULATION

There are several methods of modulating a carrier. The method which is used most is called AMPLITUDE MODULATION.

In amplitude modulation, the modulating frequency is the intelligence (voice or music) which is to be transmitted through space to receivers many miles away. This modulating frequency is audio and, by itself, cannot be transmitted. A radio-frequency wave, however, is capable of being transmitted through space. If we combine or mix an audio-frequency wave with a radio-frequency wave, we obtain an RF output which contains the audio and can be transmitted.   Figure 11-7 illustrates a voice modulated radio-frequency wave whose amplitude varies according to the amplitude of the audio wave. (Thus the term "amplitude modulation", abbreviated AM). An AM wave is, therefore, a radio-frequency wave which contains, in its amplitude variations, the audio or intelligence which we desire to transmit.

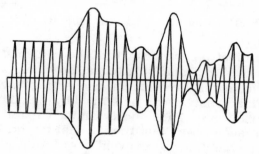

Figure 11-7. Radio wave modulated with voice.

THE AM TRANSMITTER

A block diagram of a typical amplitude modulated radiotelephone transmitter is shown in Figure 11-8. Above each block is drawn the waveshape of the voltage output of that particular stage. With the aid of these waveshapes and the block diagram layout, we shall discuss the operation of the radiotelephone transmitter.

To begin with, the oscillator stage generates a radio-frequency voltage called the carrier. Following the oscillator is the buff-

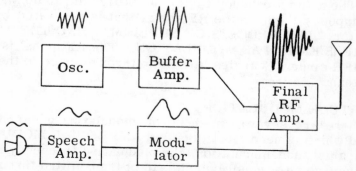

Figure 11-8. Block diagram of amplitude-modulated transmitter.

er-amplifier stage which amplifies the output of the oscillator and isolates the oscillator from the power amplifier. The final stage is the power amplifier which delivers energy to the antenna. Notice that the output waveshape of the final RF stage does not resemble the input waveshape from the buffer. The RF waveshape has been altered by modulation. This brings us to the modulation or audio section. The microphone converts the sound that is to be transmitted into electrical variations. The weak output of the microphone is fed into an audio amplifier (speech amplifier). The output of the speech amplifier is fed into an audio power amplifier called a MODULATOR. The modulator injects the audio signals into the RF power amplifier.

METHODS OF MODULATION

In the last paragraph, we discussed the general principles of amplitude modulation. We are now ready to study exactly how the audio signal is superimposed onto the carrier.

There are many different methods of amplitude modulation. The most common method is to apply the audio-frequency modulating voltage to the plate of one of the RF amplifiers. This popular method is known as PLATE MODULATION. If the audio-frequency modulating voltage is applied to the control grid of the RF amplifier, we have what is called GRID MODULATION. If a pentode power amplifier is modulated by applying the audio-frequency modulating voltage to the suppressor grid, we have SUPPRESSOR MODULATION. SCREEN GRID MODULATION AND CATHODE MODULATION can be similarly accomplished by applying the audio-frequency modulating voltage to the screen and cathode electrodes respectively. In other words, the method of modulation is determined by the electrode of the RF amplifier tube to which the audio frequency modulating voltage is applied.

Since there are several RF amplifier stages in a transmitter, a transmitter designer has his choice as to which stage should be modulated. Modulating the final RF stage of a radiotelephone transmitter is known as HIGH-LEVEL MODULATION. The term is derived from the fact that the modulation takes place at the highest power level of the transmitter. If the modulation process takes place in a stage preceding the final stage, the system is known as LOW-LEVEL MODULATION. In low-level modulation, the RF amplifiers which follow the modulated stage are operated as linear or Class A amplifiers, rather than Class C. A Class C amplifier will distort the audio component of the modulated signal, whereas a Class A amplifier will amplify all signal frequencies without distortion. If the audio component of the modulated wave is distorted, the receiver will, in turn, reproduce a distorted audio signal. In high-level modulation, the final RF amplifier is always operated as a Class C amplifier. High-level modulation is the most efficient modulating system, and is also much more popular than low-level modulation.

Most transmitters use high-level plate modulation. We will discuss this method in detail.

PLATE MODULATION

There are several variations of plate modulation. A simple one is illustrated in Figure 11-9. The audio-frequency output of the modulator stage is coupled through transformer T, to the plate

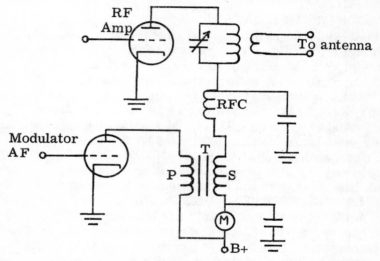

Figure 11-9. Transformer-coupled modulator circuit.

circuit of the power amplifier. Transformer T is called the modulation transformer. The audio voltage induced from the primary into the secondary winding, S, is in series with the B+ voltage which is applied to the plate of the RF power amplifier stage. Figure 11-10A shows the audio voltage.

When the audio voltage causes the top of the transformer secondary, S, to go positive with respect to the bottom, the audio voltage and the power supply voltage will aid each other. The plate voltage of the RF amplifier stage will therefore be the sum of the power supply voltage and the audio voltage. Figure 11-10B shows the rise in the RF amplifier plate voltage above the B+ value during the positive alternation of the audio. Since the plate power

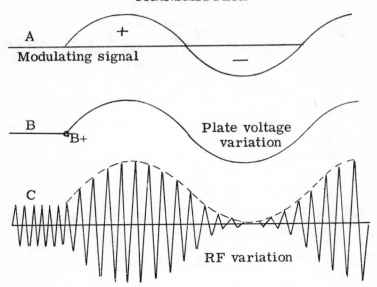

Figure 11-10. Amplitude modulation.

input to the stage is directly dependent upon the plate voltage, the plate power input will increase during the positive audio alternation. An increase in plate power input will, in turn, cause the useful power output to increase. The RF output, therefore, rises during the positive half of the audio cycle. Figure 11-10C illustrates the RF output voltage waveform before the modulating audio voltage is applied, and the resulting increase in amplitude of the RF during the positive peaks of modulation.

During the negative half of the audio cycle, the top of the transformer secondary, S, is negative with respect to the bottom. Now the audio voltage and the power supply voltage are in "series opposing". The two voltages therefore buck each other, and the plate voltage of the RF amplifier is the difference between the two voltages. Figure 11-10B shows the drop in the RF amplifier plate voltage below the B+ value during the negative alternation of the audio. The drop in plate voltage causes the plate power input to decrease. Figure 11-10C shows the resulting decrease in amplitude of the RF during the negative peaks of the audio. Figure 11-7 illustrates the RF output from a transmitter that has been modulated by speech or music.

THE PUSH-PULL MODULATOR

The single ended (one tube) modulator stage of Figure 11-9 is operated Class A so that there will be no distortion of the amplified

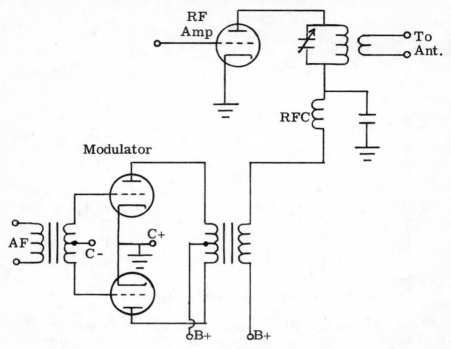

Figure 11-11. A push-pull modulator circuit.

modulating signal. The disadvantage of a one tube Class A amplifier is that it operates at low efficiency. A low efficiency tube
cannot always deliver the power that is required of a modulator
stage. A push-pull amplifier which is capable of delivering more
power than a single tube is therefore preferred. Figure 11-11 illustrates a push-pull modulator circuit.

The push-pull modulator may be operated either Class A or
Class B, depending upon the power output requirements.

A Class B push-pull amplifier requires a large driving power
applied to its grid circuit. The positive peaks of the grid signal
usually drive the grid into grid current. A flow of grid current
causes power to be dissipated in the grid circuit and the driver
stage must be able to supply this power.

A push-pull amplifier, operated Class A, does not operate in
the grid current region and therefore, requires very little grid
driving power from the driver stage. The Class A push-pull amplifier amplifies the audio modulating voltage without distortion.
The Class B modulator introduces a certain amount of distortion
into the modulating signal.

CHAPTER 12

DETECTION

It has been pointed out in a previous chapter that the detector is the heart of the receiver. It is the detector that extracts the audio intelligence from the signal that enters the receiver. Actually, a detector, by itself, can be considered as a simple type of receiver.

In this chapter, we shall study four different types of detection: diode detection, plate detection, grid-leak detection and regenerative detection.

THE DIODE DETECTOR

Figure 12-1 illustrates a diode detector. With its antenna, ground and headphones, it is a simple one-tube receiver. Let us see how this circuit operates.

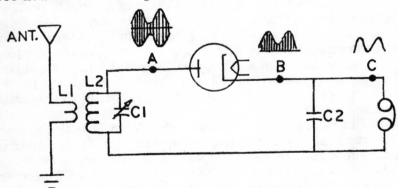

Figure 12-1. Diode detector.

The radio frequency waves radiated by the transmitter cut across the receiver antenna and induce a signal voltage into it. This RF signal is brought down into coil L1, by means of the transmission line that connects the antenna to the receiver. Because of the coupling between L1 and L2, the signal is induced into L2. L2 and C1 form a resonant circuit. By varying C1, we can make this circuit resonant to any one of a great many frequencies. Since each broadcast station transmits a signal on a different frequency, we can use C1 to tune in the station that we wish to listen to.

Once we choose the desired signal, we can then proceed to

"detect" the information in this signal. In Figure 12-1, we show the waveshape of the signal as it appears at different points of the circuit. Notice the wave at point A, the output of the tuned circuit. The upper half is exactly the same as the lower half. Since the audio is represented by a line joining the peaks of the wave, we actually have the audio duplicated in the upper and lower halves of the signal. Either the upper or the lower part of the signal must be removed because the upper audio signal, which is positive, and the lower audio signal, which is negative, would cancel each other when the RF component of the signal is removed. Removing the upper or lower half of the signal will in no way harm the audio intelligence, since each half of the signal contains the complete audio information.

Cancelling one half of the signal is accomplished by means of the principle of rectification. The entire RF signal is simply a high frequency AC signal, and we use a diode vacuum tube or semiconductor to remove the lower half of the signal. (It doesn't make any difference which half of the signal is removed). Rectification of the RF signal is accomplished in the following manner: When the positive half of the signal drives the plate of the diode positive with respect to the cathode, the tube conducts and current flows through the circuit. When the negative half of the signal drives the plate of the diode negative with respect to the cathode, the tube will not conduct and current will not flow through the circuit during this half of the cycle. The lower half of the RF signal will therefore be cut off and does not appear at the output of the detector tube. (See Figure 12-1).

We still have not extracted the audio from the RF carrier. This is accomplished by C2, a low value capacitor in the order of .0001 mfd. The signal across C2 consists of two components: the low frequency audio intelligence and the high frequency RF carrier. Because a low value capacitor has a low reactance to the high frequency RF, the RF component will be shorted by the capacitor and will not appear in the headphones. Because C2 has a high reactance to the low audio frequencies, the audio will not be shorted and will appear in the headphones. Thus we have succeeded in extracting the audio intelligence from the RF carrier by means of the diode detector.

THE PLATE DETECTOR

The diode detector just described is commonly used. However, it has one disadvantage - it can only detect; it cannot amplify the signal that it has detected. Additional stages of amplification are necessary. The plate detector shown in Figure 12-2 is both a detector and an amplifier.

Its operation is similar to the diode detector in that it rectifies the incoming RF signal and then filters out the RF from the signal. Rectification occurs in the following manner: The plate current flows through R1 and creates a voltage drop or grid bias across it. The resistor value is chosen to provide a bias sufficiently negative to cut the tube off when no RF signal is applied to the circuit.

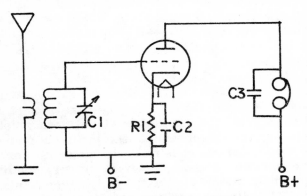

Figure 12-2.   Plate detector.

When the signal is applied to the circuit, the positive half of the signal overcomes part of the negative bias and causes plate current to flow. When the negative half of the incoming signal appears at the grid, the plate current stops flowing since the negative signal voltage adds to the bias voltage, making the grid more negative. Since the positive half of the signal is reproduced and the negative half is eliminated, we have succeeded in rectifying the signal.

The RF is filtered out of the signal by C2 in the same manner as in the diode detector.   The audio component is then applied to the earphones.

THE GRID-LEAK DETECTOR

The grid-leak detector is actually a combination of a diode detector and an amplifier. This can easily be realized by looking at the grid-leak detector in Figure 12-3. Consider the grid as the plate of the diode detector. The grid-leak resistor, R1, acts as the load of the diode detector in the same manner as the earphones of Figure 1.

When a modulated RF signal is applied to the grid-leak detector, current flows from cathode to grid and through the grid circuit only on the positive halves of the signal.

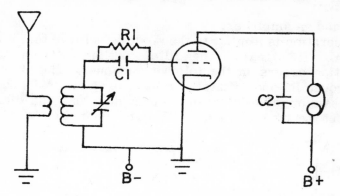

Figure 12-3.   Grid-leak detector.

This is because a negative grid, just like a negative plate, will repel the electrons.   The incoming signal is thus rectified.

C1 filters out the RF component of the incoming signal and the audio intelligence appears across the grid-leak resistor, R1. The audio signal across the grid-leak resistor acts as the bias of the triode tube, and the plate current will vary in accordance with the voltage across R1.   Because of the amplification property of a triode, we find that the audio developed in the plate circuit, across the headsets, is much larger than that across the grid-leak resistor. Capacitor C2 filters out any RF that might appear in the plate circuit.

While the grid-leak detector has more gain than the plate detector, it has the disadvantage of being easily overloaded by strong RF signals and causing distortion of its output.

THE REGENERATIVE DETECTOR

Figure 12-4 illustrates a regenerative detector. You will notice that it is similar to the grid-leak detector.   The only difference is that a coil has been added in the plate circuit. This coil, L2, is called the TICKLER coil.   It is magnetically coupled to the grid coil, L3.

When the incoming modulated RF signal enters the circuit, it is detected in the grid circuit the same as it is in a grid-leak detector.   However, because L2 is coupled to L3, some of the amplified signal in the plate circuit is fed back to the grid circuit to be reamplified.   This increases the amplification of the circuit considerably.

It is important that the tickler coil be placed in such a position with respect to the grid coil that the signal fed back to the grid coil is in phase with the incoming signal.   In this way, the feed-

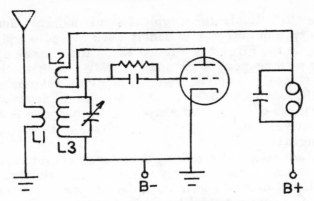

Figure 12-4. Regenerative detector.

back voltage will add to the incoming signal voltage. If the feedback voltage is out of phase with the incoming signal, it will cancel
some of the incoming signal and reduce the amplification.

The regenerative detector is the most sensitive triode detector and is capable of receiving signals over long distances.

THE SOLID-STATE DETECTOR

Although Figure 12-1 shows a tube used as a diode detector,
solid-state detectors are more commonly employed, for a number
of reasons. Unlike a tube, a semiconductor does not require filament voltage. Semiconductor crystal diodes are also light in
weight, do not require a socket, and can be wired into position as
easily as any resistor. Also, since no heating time is needed,
crystal diodes work immediately.

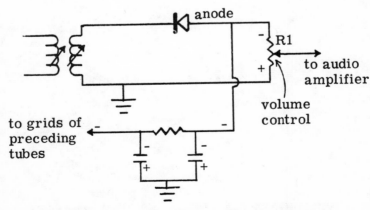

Figure 12-5. A solid-state detector circuit.

Figure 12-5 illustrates a typical semiconductor detector circuit. This type of detector is widely used in radio and television receivers. In the circuit of Figure 12-5, the voltage at the anode is negative with respect to ground. It is fed back to the grids of preceding stages to control their gain. This system is known as AUTOMATIC GAIN CONTROL. It is similar to automatic volume control (described in the next chapter). Its purpose is to keep the output of the receiver constant, regardless of the strength of the incoming signals.

The disadvantage of the diode detector, whether tube or semiconductor, is that a diode has no amplification. However, modern receivers have adequate gain in other stages. The diode is used because of its excellent fidelity characteristics.

CHAPTER 13

THE TRF RECEIVER

INTRODUCTION

A radio frequency signal diminishes in strength at a very rapid rate after it leaves the transmitting antenna. When it reaches the receiving antenna, it is very weak -- so weak that it is seldom possible for a detector circuit (unaided) to produce a useful output from it. To remedy this, it is desirable to amplify the signal before and after it is detected. This is accomplished by the use of an RF amplifier before the detector and an audio frequency (AF) amplifier after the detector.

The RF amplifier, like the detector, is provided with one or more tuned circuits. This enables it to select and amplify the desired signal only. Thus, the addition of an RF amplifier to the detector not only increases sensitivity (ability to receive weak signals), but also gives greater selectivity (ability to separate signals).

The output of the detector stage is followed by one or more stages of AF amplification. If a headset is to be used, only one stage of audio amplification is necessary. If a speaker is to be used, two or more stages of audio amplification will be necessary.

The complete receiver, consisting of one or more radio frequency amplifiers, detector, and one or more audio frequency amplifiers, is called a TUNED RADIO FREQUENCY receiver, or simply, a TRF receiver. A block diagram of a TRF receiver, together with the waveform of the signal at each stage, is shown in Figure 13-1.

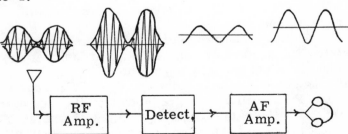

Figure 13-1. Block diagram of a TRF receiver.

THE RF AMPLIFIER

The RF amplifier, as previously stated, gives the receiver desired selectivity and sensitivity required for satisfactory recep-

155

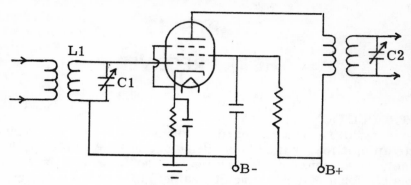

Figure 13-2. RF stage of amplification.

tion. Figure 13-2 illustrates an RF stage of amplification. You will note that essentially it consists of a tuned circuit (L1C1) that selects the desired signal, and a tube that amplifies the signal. The important operating characteristics of the amplifier are as follows:

(1) The RF amplifier tube is biased to operate as a Class A voltage amplifier. We do this because a Class A amplifier will amplify the signal without distorting it. It is important not to distort the signal at this point since it contains the audio intelligence.

(2) The tube used in the RF amplifier is generally a pentode because of its low interelectrode capacitances. If a triode, with its high interelectrode capacitances were used, there would be sufficient feedback from plate to grid at radio frequencies to cause the RF amplifier to oscillate. An oscillating amplifier would cause serious distortion, making satisfactory reception almost impossible.

(3) Self-bias is almost always used in an RF amplifier. A cathode biasing resistor and a cathode by-pass capacitor provide the bias for the tube.

(4) The RF transformer consists of a primary coil and a secondary coil. The secondary coil is designed to cover the desired frequency range when tuned by capacitor C1.

At the height of their popularity, most TRF receivers used two or three RF amplifier stages ahead of the detector. Each stage is tuned to the same frequency. Since it would be impractical to tune each of the stages individually, we mount all the tuning capacitors on a common shaft so that all the RF stages can be tuned simultaneously. Capacitors mounted on a common shaft in this manner are said to be "ganged".

In order that each stage be tuned to the exact same frequency at any setting of the ganged capacitors, the capacitors and coils

in each stage should be identical. However, because of manufacturing tolerances and stray capacitances and inductances, this is
not possible. In order to compensate for the small differences in
value of the tuned circuit components, small variable capacitors,
called trimmers, are placed across the tuning capacitors. These
trimmers are mounted at the side of the tuning capacitors and
their capacitances can be varied with an alignment tool. Figure
13-3 illustrates a 3-gang tuning capacitor with its trimmers. We

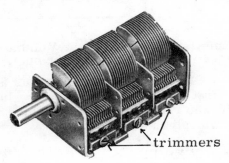

trimmers

Figure 13-3. A 3-gang tuning capacitor with trimmers.

adjust the trimmers so that each one of the RF amplifier stages
tunes to the same frequency at any particular setting of the station
selector knob. The process of adjusting the trimmers is called
"ALIGNMENT" and when the receiver is properly aligned, it has
maximum gain and selectivity.

VOLUME CONTROL

Some method of controlling the volume of a radio receiver is
necessary since the signals arriving at the receiver antenna vary
in their intensity. There are many methods of controlling the
volume. Some control the gain of the RF stages and are referred
to as RF gain controls; others vary the output of the detector.

Figure 13-4 illustrates a method of controlling the volume by
varying the grid bias of an RF amplifier stage. The tube that is
used is so constructed that its amplification varies as the bias is
varied. We call this type of tube a variable-mu tube. Thus, as
we change the value of Rc, the grid bias of the tube varies, causing the amplification of the stage to vary. This raises or lowers
the volume of the receiver's audio output.

Figure 13-5 illustrates another method of controlling the volume of a receiver. The variable resistor R1 is both the load of
the diode detector and the volume control. The entire audio output
of the detector is across R1. By sliding the arm of the potenti-

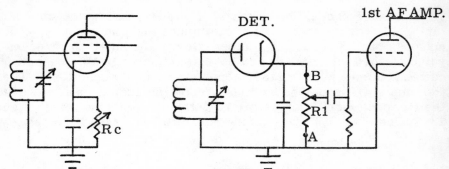

Figure 13-4. Volume
control in RF stage.

Figure 13-5. Volume control
in detector stage.

ometer from A to B, we tap off varying amounts of audio and apply
it to the grid of the first audio amplifier stage. In this way, we
control the volume of the receiver. The technique in Figure 13-5
is the one that is commonly used.

CIRCUIT OF A TRF RECEIVER

Figure 13-6 shows the schematic diagram of a four-tube TRF
receiver. The receiver consists of two RF stages, a diode detector stage and an audio amplifier stage. The power supply is not
shown. You will note that while transformer coupling is used between the RF stages, resistance coupling is used between the detector stage and the audio amplifier stage. Resistance coupling is
used in the audio section because of its simplicity and because it
gives better fidelity than transformer coupling. The dotted lines
connecting the three tuning capacitors indicate that these capacitors are ganged.

The following table indicates the function of each component
shown in Figure 13-6.

V1, V2	RF Amplifier Tubes
V3	Diode Detector Tube
V4	Audio Amplifier Tube
T1, T2, T3	RF Transformers
T4	Audio Output Transformer
R1, R3, R7	Cathode Bias Resistors
R2, R4	Screen Voltage Dropping Resistors
R5	Volume Control and Diode Detector Load Resistor
R6	Grid Load Resistor
C1, C5, C9	Tuning Capacitors
C2, C6, C10	Trimmer Capacitors
C3, C7, C13	Cathode By-Pass Capacitors
C4, C8	Screen By-Pass Capacitors

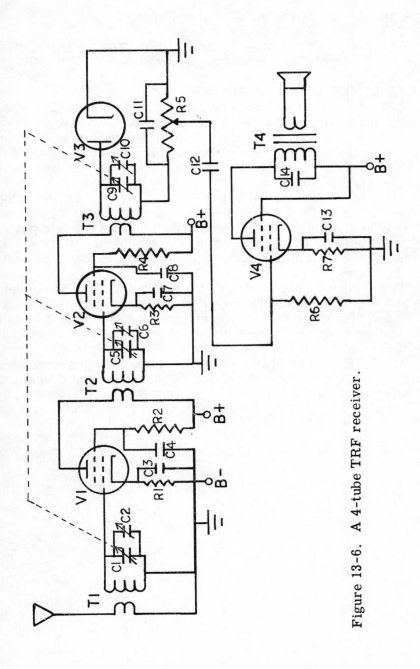

Figure 13-6. A 4-tube TRF receiver.

C11   Detector RF Filter Capacitor
C12   Audio Coupling Capacitor
C14   Capacitor To Bypass High Audio Frequencies
                  (tone control capacitor)

CAPABILITIES OF A TRF RECEIVER

A TRF receiver will operate in a satisfactory manner when it is used for a single low frequency RF band. However, it is not satisfactory when used for high frequencies or over a wide range of frequencies. At the higher frequencies, a TRF receiver has difficulty picking one signal apart from another. In other words, its selectivity is poor.

Also, the amplification of the RF amplifier is low at the higher frequencies. This limits the reception of the TRF receiver. Not only are the gain and selectivity of the TRF poor, but they vary considerably from one frequency to another. It is difficult to design an RF amplifier whose gain and selectivity are constant over its tuning range.

These disadvantages of the TRF receiver led to the development of the superheterodyne type of receiver. The principles of the superheterodyne type of receiver and how it overcomes the disadvantages of the TRF receiver are fully discussed in the next chapter.

The TRF receiver has now been replaced by the more sensitive and more selective superheterodyne receiver, described in the next chapter.

CHAPTER 14

THE SUPERHETERODYNE RECEIVER

GENERAL THEORY OF THE SUPERHETERODYNE RECEIVER
   The detector stage in a superheterodyne receiver is similar to the detector stage in a TRF receiver. The audio section is also the same. The differences between the two receivers lie in the stages preceding the detector.
   In the TRF receiver, all the RF stages are tuned to the frequency of the incoming signal and the signal is thus amplified. This is not true in the superheterodyne receiver. Here, the incoming signal is first changed to a LOW FIXED frequency and is then amplified and detected. The new low fixed frequency is called the Intermediate Frequency (IF). In changing the incoming signal to the Intermediate Frequency, we do not in any way disturb the audio intelligence in the signal.
   By amplifying the lower, fixed signal, it is possible to use circuits that have greater selectivity and sensitivity than those used in TRF receivers.

THE HETERODYNE PRINCIPLE OF GENERATING A FIXED IF SIGNAL
   In our study of modulation, we learned that two different frequencies, when mixed together, will generate two new frequencies. The new frequencies are the sum and difference of the original frequencies. This principle is made use of in the superheterodyne.
   The superheterodyne contains a variable oscillator stage that generates an RF signal. This RF signal is mixed together with the incoming RF signal to give the new Intermediate Frequency signal. Let us see how this works with actual examples: We will assume that we are listening to a station whose frequency is 1000 kc. The oscillator stage is then set to generate a signal whose frequency is 1456 kc. These two signals are mixed together and two new frequencies are produced: 456 kc. (the difference of the original two frequencies) and 2456 kc. (the sum of the original two frequencies). We disregard the 2456 kc. signal and amplify and detect the 456 kc. signal, which is the intermediate frequency signal. Let us assume that we desire to change to a new station whose frequency is 1300 kc. We then change the oscillator frequency to 1756 kc. The difference between the two frequencies is still 456 kc. and this signal is then fed to the IF amplifiers. The

IF amplifiers are tuned to the IF frequency (456 kc.) and amplify only this one frequency. No matter what station we tune to, the difference between the incoming signal frequency and the oscillator frequency is always the same. In the above example, the IF was 456 kc. Most receivers use this frequency for the IF. A few receivers use other frequencies.

THE SUPERHETERODYNE RECEIVER
    Figure 14-1 shows the block diagram of a typical superheterodyne receiver. The graphical form of the signal passing through the receiver is also shown. We will now study the operation of the superheterodyne receiver by following the signal through its stages.

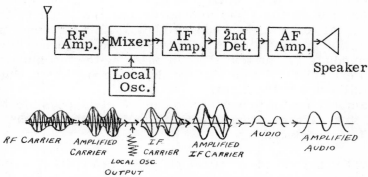

Figure 14-1. Block diagram of a superheterodyne receiver.

    From the antenna the incoming signal goes to the RF amplifier. Here it is selected and amplified in the same manner as in a TRF receiver. It is then passed on to the MIXER stage. The mixer stage "MIXES" the RF signal with a signal generated by the local oscillator. The mixer is called a CONVERTER and sometimes, a FIRST DETECTOR.
    The mixing action of the mixer stage produces two new modulated RF signals, in addition to the original two signals. They are the sum and the difference of the signal frequency and the oscillator frequency. It is the difference or intermediate frequency in which we are interested. Therefore, in the output of the mixer stage there is a circuit, fixed-tuned to the intermediate frequency which rejects all other frequencies. The new IF signal contains all the modulation characteristics of the original signal.
    The IF signal is then fed to the IF amplifier stage where it is amplified. From here the signal goes to the detector, which is similar in operation to the detector of the TRF receiver. We

sometimes refer to this stage as the second detector since we can consider the mixer stage as the first detector. After the audio is extracted from the modulated carrier, it is amplified by an audio amplifier stage.

Thus, we have briefly traced a signal through a superheterodyne receiver. We shall now discuss in more detail, the operation of the various stages and circuits of the superheterodyne receiver.

FREQUENCY CONVERSION

The combined circuits of the mixer stage and oscillator stage form the frequency converter. As we previously pointed out, the purpose of the frequency converter is to convert the incoming signal to a low fixed frequency (the intermediate frequency) which is then passed onto the IF amplifiers. There are a large number of possible combinations of tubes and circuits which may be used for frequency conversion. These various combinations may be broken down into two different types: (1) Circuits using a separate mixer tube and oscillator tube and (2) Circuits using one tube for both the oscillator and mixer stages. We shall now study each type in detail.

Figure 14-2 illustrates a frequency conversion circuit using a triode mixer stage and a separate triode oscillator stage. An Armstrong oscillator circuit is used. Practically any type of oscillator could be used.

The output of the oscillator is fed or injected into the grid of the mixer through a coupling capacitor, C. This is called grid injection. The oscillator output can also be injected into the cath-

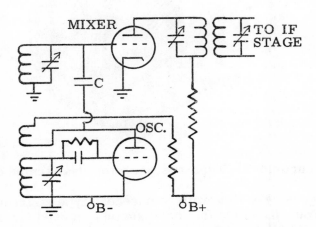

Figure 14-2. Frequency conversion using two tubes.

ode of the mixer. The coil and capacitor in the mixer grid circuit are tuned to the frequency of the incoming signal. The coil and capacitor in the oscillator grid circuit are tuned to a frequency higher or lower than the signal frequency by an amount equal to the intermediate frequency. The plate circuit of the mixer stage is fixed tuned to the intermediate frequency. An example will clarify this point: Let us assume that the incoming signal has a frequency of 1000 kc. and the intermediate frequency of the receiver is 456 kc. The oscillator would then be tuned to 1456 kc. (The oscillator could also be tuned to 544 kc., but practically all receivers tune the oscillator frequency above that of the incoming signal). The oscillator signal and the incoming signal mix together in the mixer tube and produce the intermediate frequency of 456 kc. Now let us assume that we wish to receive an incoming signal at 1200 kc. We must tune the mixer grid circuit to 1200 kc. and, at the same time, we must tune the oscillator to 1656 kc. These two frequencies will mix together in the mixer tube to produce the 456 kc. IF. In order to tune the oscillator tank circuit and the mixer tank circuit at the same time, both tuning capacitors are on the same shaft and are both rotated when we change stations on the receiver. The two capacitors are said to be ganged. Figure 14-3 shows a typical superheterodyne tuning capacitor. The smaller section is the oscillator capacitor and the larger section is the mixer capacitor.

Figure 14-3.   Typical superheterodyne tuning capacitor.

Figure 14-4 illustrates our second type of frequency conversion. You will notice that only one tube is used for both the mixer and the oscillator. The tube has five grids and is called a pentagrid converter. The cathode, grid 1 and grid 2 act as the cathode,

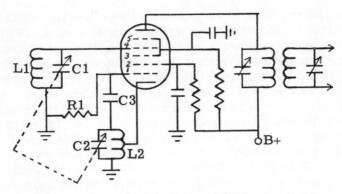

Figure 14-4. The pentagrid converter.

control grid and plate of the oscillator section respectively. The oscillator is a Hartley type of oscillator. L2 is the oscillator coil and C2 is the oscillator tuning capacitor. R1 and C3 are the oscillator grid leak resistor and capacitor. Grid 4 acts as the mixer grid. It receives the incoming signal from the mixer tuned circuit, L1-C1. Grids 3 and 5 are connected together within the tube. They serve as the screen of the mixer and also as an electrostatic shield between the oscillator and mixer sections of the pentagrid converter.

The oscillator output is actually coupled to the mixer section by means of the tube's electron stream. We can consider the cathode and the first two grids as a composite cathode which supplies to the rest of the tube, an electron stream that varies at the oscillator frequency. The incoming signal voltage that is applied to grid 4, further controls the electron stream so that the plate current variations are a combination of the oscillator and the incoming signal frequencies. The plate circuit of the pentagrid converter is tuned to the difference of the two frequencies, the intermediate frequency.

MIXERS AND CONVERTERS

Although these two words, mixers and converters, are often used interchangeably, there is a difference. A single tube may be used to work both as a local oscillator and a mixer. It is then known as a converter, such as the one shown in Figure 14-4. If separate tubes are used, one is referred to as the local oscillator while the other is called the mixer, as shown earlier in Fig. 14-2.

I. F. AMPLIFIERS

The IF amplifier is a high gain stage that is permanently tuned to the frequency difference between the incoming signal and the local oscillator. Pentode tubes are generally used as IF amplifiers because of their high gain and low interelectrode capacitances. We desire low interelectrode capacitances to prevent the IF amplifiers from breaking into oscillation. The IF section of the superheterodyne receiver consists of one or more stages, with each stage adjusted to tune to the IF frequency. Since all incoming signals are converted to the same frequency by the mixer, the IF amplifier operates at only one frequency. The tuned circuits, therefore, are designed for maximum gain and for the desired selectivity. It is in the IF section that practically all the voltage gain and selectivity of the superheterodyne are developed.

The diagram of an IF amplifier stage is shown in Figure 14-5. Note T1 and T2. They are called IF transformers. The dotted lines around them indicate that the IF transformers are in metal cans. The cans act as shields and prevent oscillation. Double-tuned IF transformers are used in practically all radio receivers.

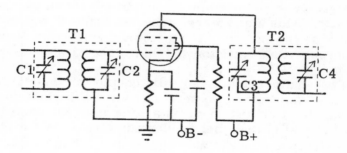

Figure 14-5. IF stage.

The tuned circuits of Figure 14-5 are adjusted to the exact IF frequency by means of the variable capacitors, C1, C2, C3 and C4. These capacitors are actually small trimmers located inside the transformer can. There are two holes in the transformer can that allow a small screwdriver to reach through the can and adjust the trimmers. In recent years, radio manufacturers have been using IF transformers that have fixed capacitors and variable inductors. The inductors use a powdered iron core and we tune the transformers by moving the core in and out of the coil. This is called PERMEABILITY TUNING.

Most AM (amplitude modulated) radio receivers use an intermediate frequency of 456 kc. This has been selected as a compromise between a lower and a higher value. The lower the IF, the greater is the gain and selectivity. However, a low intermediate frequency allows the receiver to pick up some stations at 2 points on the dial. This results in interference. If we use a high IF, we overcome this defect, but we lose gain and selectivity. An IF of 456 kc. has been chosen by most receiver manufacturers, though some receivers have their IF's as low as 100 kc. and as high as 15,000 kc.

SECOND DETECTORS

The "second detector" of the superheterodyne receiver is the actual detector of the set. It is here that we extract the audio intelligence from the RF carrier. We call it a "second detector" because we sometimes refer to the frequency converter as the "first detector".

Figure 14-6 illustrates the diagram of a second detector used in a superheterodyne. The second detector and the first audio frequency amplifier are combined in one envelope. This is done in most receivers to save tubes and space. The plate, P1 and the cathode are the diode detector portion of the receiver. The plate, P2, the grid and the cathode represent the first audio frequency amplifier stage.

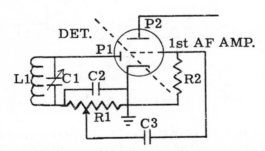

Figure 14-6. Second detector and first AF stage.

The detector of Figure 14-6 operates in the same manner as all diode detectors. The explanation in Chapter 11 applies here. L1-C1 is the secondary tuned circuit of the last IF transformer. It is also the tuned circuit of the detector. R1 is the detector load resistor across which the audio appears. By using it as a voltage divider to tap off various amounts of audio, we control the volume of the receiver. C2 is the capacitor that filters out the RF. C3 is an audio coupling capacitor that couples the audio from the detector to the grid of the first AF amplifier. R2 is the grid load resistor.

In spite of the diode detector's lack of amplification, it is used in practically all modern superheterodyne receivers because of its excellent fidelity. Sufficient amplification is provided by the other stages.

AUTOMATIC VOLUME CONTROL

Controlling the volume by varying the load resistor of the diode detector is a simple satisfactory method. However, by itself, this method leaves a certain amount to be desired. For instance, every time we change from one station to another of different signal strength, we must reset the volume control. It would be far better to set the volume control at a desired level and have the audio output remain constant, regardless of the strength of the incoming signal. This can be accomplished by means of a system known as AUTOMATIC VOLUME CONTROL. Figure 14-7 shows a circuit using this system.

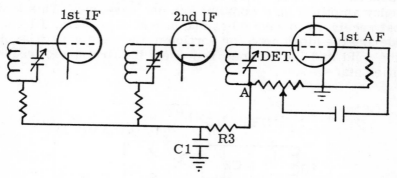

Figure 14-7. Automatic volume control circuit.

In the system of automatic volume control (abbreviated AVC), we automatically reduce the strength of the strong signals and build up the strength of the weak signals. This is accomplished in the following manner:

The audio output voltage of the diode detector is developed at point A of Figure 14-7. This voltage varies directly with the strength of the incoming signal. As the strength of the incoming signal increases, the audio voltage at point A increases; as the strength of the incoming signal decreases, the audio voltage at point A decreases. The audio voltage at point A is fed back through a filter (C1, R3) to the grids of the IF amplifiers. (This voltage can also be fed to the grid of the RF amplifier if the superheterodyne has one). In other words, this voltage is applied as bias to the grids of the IF and RF stages.

The tubes used in the IF and RF stages are variable-mu tubes. A variable-mu tube is so constructed that its amplification varies inversely with its bias. As the bias on the grid of a variable-mu tube is made more negative, the amplification of the tube is decreased; and, as the bias is made less negative, the amplification is increased.

We shall now see how all these factors operate to keep the output level of the receiver constant. Let us assume that we are listening to a certain station and have set the volume control to the desired audio output. We then change to a station whose incoming signal is stronger than the first station. This station will produce a larger audio voltage at point A of Figure 14-7 than the previous station. This larger negative voltage will be fed back to the grids of the variable-mu amplifier tubes. The increased negative bias will reduce the amplification of the tubes and therefore, the gain of their stages will be reduced. This reduction in the gain of the receiver will compensate for the increased signal strength and will keep the audio output level constant.

Now, let us assume that we tune to a station whose signal strength is weak. There will be a low voltage at point A of Figure 14-7. The negative grid bias of the variable-mu tubes will decrease and the amplification of the tubes will automatically increase. This will increase the overall gain of the receiver and bring the audio output of this weak signal up to the output level of the other signals.

The function of R3, C1 is to filter out the audio variations and keep them from being fed back to the IF and RF stages. All that we want to feed back are the slower variations resulting from changes in the incoming signal strengths and not the audio variations.

RF AMPLIFIERS AND IMAGES

The more expensive superheterodyne receivers contain one or two RF amplifiers ahead of the mixer. An RF amplifier will increase the gain and selectivity of the receiver. It will also reduce the reception of IMAGES. An image is an UNWANTED signal that differs in frequency from the local oscillator frequency by an amount equal to the intermediate frequency. For instance, if we are tuned to 1000 kc. and the IF is 456 kc., then the oscillator frequency would be 1456 kc. Assume there was a station at 1912 kc. The signal of this station would appear at the grid of the converter and beat with the oscillator to produce the IF of 456 kc. This signal would be heard, in addition to the 1000 kc. signal that we are tuned to. We call 1912 kc. the image frequency. By adding a tuned RF amplifier ahead of the mixer, we reduce the reception of images. This is because the RF amplifier is tuned to the frequency of the station that we wish to listen to and it is difficult for the image frequency to get through the additional tuned circuits. Without the RF amplifier, the image frequency has only to get through the mixer tuned circuits.

The circuit of an RF amplifier used in a superheterodyne receiver is the same as those discussed in Chapter 12. The variable capacitor in the grid circuit of the RF amplifier is ganged together with the mixer capacitor and the oscillator capacitor.

ALIGNMENT

In addition to the ganged variable capacitor, there are also a number of small variable capacitors (trimmers or padders) and variable inductors found in a superheterodyne. Their function is to correct for any variations that may exist in the tuned circuits. When the station selector knob is turned, the various RF stages must all tune to the same frequency and the local oscillator frequency must vary in such a manner that the frequency difference between the local oscillator and the RF stages is always equal to the intermediate frequency. When the circuits are adjusted in this manner, they are said to be TRACKING. It is also necessary to adjust the IF stages so that they all tune to the intermediate frequency. When all circuits are correctly tuned, we say that the receiver is properly aligned. Misalignment in any stage of a superheterodyne will cause a decrease in sensitivity or selectivity, or both.

In order to align a superheterodyne receiver, a calibrated oscillator or signal generator and some form of output indicator are needed.

A signal from the signal generator is injected into the receiver at various points and we tune the trimmers or variable inductors of the various circuits for maximum reading on the output indicator.

A TYPICAL SUPERHETERODYNE RECEIVER

The circuit diagram of a typical AC/DC superheterodyne is shown in Figure 14-8. Each component part of the circuit is labeled. The table below, showing the function of each part, will serve as an excellent review of the theory of the superheterodyne receiver.

PART	VALUE	FUNCTION
V1		Pentagrid converter tube
V2		IF amplifier tube
V3		2nd detector, AVC and 1st audio fre-

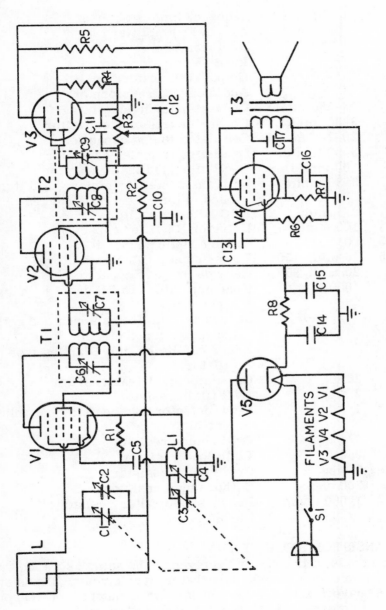

Figure 14-8. A typical AC/DC superheterodyne receiver.

PART	VALUE	FUNCTION
		quency amplifier tube.
V4		AF power amplifier tube
V5		Rectifier tube
T1		Input IF transformer
T2		Output IF transformer
T3		Audio output transformer
C1	15-350 mmfd.	Converter tuning capacitor
C2	3-30 mmfd.	Converter trimmer capacitor
C3	10-200 mmfd.	Oscillator tuning capacitor
C4	3-30 mmfd.	Oscillator trimmer capacitor
C5	100 mmfd.	Oscillator grid leak capacitor
C6, C7, C8, C9	3-30 mmfd.	IF transformer trimmer capacitors - used in alignment of IF stages
C10	0.5 mfd.	AVC filter capacitor
C11	100 mmfd.	Detector RF filter capacitor
C12, C13	.01 mfd.	Audio coupling capacitors
C14, C15	16 mfd. 150V.	Power supply filter capacitors
C16	20 mfd. 25V.	Cathode by-pass capacitor
C17	1000 mmfd.	Tone capacitor - to filter out high audio frequencies
L		Serves as both loop antenna and coil of converter tuned circuit
L1		Local oscillator coil (Hartley type oscillator)
R1	25K	Oscillator grid-leak resistor
R2	2 Meg.	AVC filter resistor
R3	1/2 Meg.	Diode detector load resistor and volume control
R4	1/2 Meg.	Grid return resistor
R5	250K	Plate load resistor
R6	5 Meg.	Grid return resistor
R7	200 ohms	Cathode bias resistor
R8	1,000 ohms	Power supply filter resistor
S1		On-off switch

THE TRANSISTOR RECEIVER

Circuitwise, a transistor receiver is the same as a tube-type receiver, since both use the superheterodyne circuit. Transistor receivers have become very popular for a number of reasons. They can be constructed much more compactly than tube type sets and so, are in demand where portability is important. Unlike tube sets which require a certain amount of warmup time, transistor sets operate immediately.

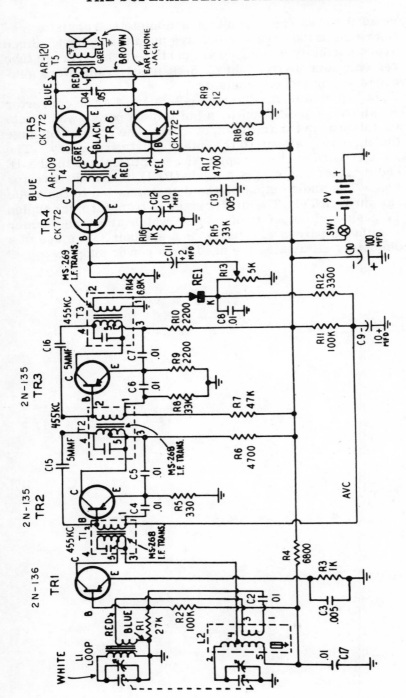

Fig. 14-9. A six transistor broadcast receiver (courtesy Lafayette)

Figure 14-9 shows the circuit of a complete transistor receiver. Note that triode transistors are used throughout. Since tube receivers normally use high-gain pentodes, the average tube set requires only four or five tubes. Sets using transistors generally average six or more transistors.

The first transistor in Figure 14-9 is used in a converter stage. The signal is picked up by a built-in loopstick which acts both as an antenna and a tuned input coil. The converter stage changes the incoming signal to the intermediate frequency. The second and third transistors supply the amplification in the IF stages. The detector stage uses a diode (RE1) in a diode detector arrangement. The audio output of the detector is fed to the audio driver stage through C11. The driver stage is transformer coupled to a pair of push-pull output transistors, which are transformer coupled to either a pair of earphones or a speaker. The use of a battery completely eliminates the need for a power supply.

CHAPTER 15

ANTENNAS

ANTENNA RADIATION

Once an RF signal has been generated in a transmitter, some means must be provided for radiating this RF energy into space. This is accomplished by the transmitting antenna. The transmitting antenna provides the link or impedance matching device between the output stage of the transmitter and space. The RF output, in the form of an electromagnetic field, travels through space and cuts across a receiving antenna, inducing a voltage in it. If the receiver is tuned to the same frequency as the transmitter, the signal will be received and heard.

PRINCIPLES OF RADIATION

The currents flowing in the antenna, due to the excitation from the transmitter, set up magnetic and electrostatic fields which are pushed out from the antenna and fly off into space in all directions. The two fields, moving through space as an electromagnetic wave, have the following characteristics:

(1) The wave has a very definite frequency which is equal to the carrier frequency of the transmitter.

(2) The wave travels through space at a constant velocity, regardless of the frequency at which it is being transmitted. This velocity is 186,000 miles per second, or 3×10^8 meters per second. ($3 \times 10^8 = 300,000,000$).

(3) The wave has a certain wavelength which is defined as the distance the wave travels through space during one cycle of the antenna voltage or current. The wavelength is measured in meters and is given the symbol "λ". λ = wavelength in meters. λ is the Greek letter "Lambda".

(4) An equation which ties together wavelength, frequency and velocity of an electromagnetic wave, is given below:

$$V = F\lambda$$

where: V is the velocity of the electromagnetic wave in free space
$V = 3 \times 10^8$ meters per second
F is the frequency of the wave in cycles per second
λ is the wavelength in meters

If the frequency is in kilocycles per second, the formula becomes: (2) F (kc) x λ (meters) = 300,000

175

If we wish to solve for the wavelength, the formula becomes:

$$(3) \quad \lambda \text{(meters)} = \frac{300,000}{F \text{(kc)}}$$

If we wish to solve for the frequency, the formula becomes:

$$(4) \quad F \text{ (in kc. per second)} = \frac{300,000}{\lambda \text{(meters)}}$$

FOR EXAMPLE:

(a) Find the wavelength of the distress frequency, 500 kc.

SOLUTION: Use formula No. 3.

$$\lambda \text{(meters)} = \frac{300,000}{F \text{ (kc.)}} = \frac{300,000}{500} = 600 \text{ meters}$$

(b) Find the wavelength of the frequency 1500 kc.

SOLUTION: Use formula No. 4.

$$\lambda \text{(meters)} = \frac{300,000}{F \text{ (kc.)}} = \frac{300,000}{1500} = 200 \text{ meters}$$

Radio waves today are designated in frequency rather than in wavelength; for example, you talk about a 30 megacycle carrier frequency, rather than a 10 meter carrier wavelength. However, wavelength figures are very convenient in the discussion of antenna systems because the wavelength gives some indication of the actual physical dimension of the antenna. For example, a half wave antenna for 10 meter transmission is 5 meters long, or converting to yard units, approximately 5-1/2 yards.

FUNDAMENTAL ANTENNA CONSIDERATIONS

Figure 15-1 shows an antenna connected to an RF source. The alternating current starts from point A and travels out along the wire until it reaches point B. The wave cannot continue further and bounces back, or is reflected, from point B (Figure 15-2). The distance an RF wave travels during the period of one cycle is known as the wavelength. If the wave is to travel exactly the length

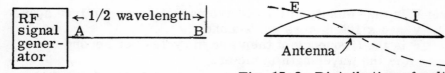

Fig. 15-1. Half-wave antenna.

Fig. 15-2. Distribution of voltage and current on half-wave antenna.

of the wire and back during the period of one cycle, it is evident that the wire must be equal in length to one-half the wavelength of the voltage being applied. The wire is then said to be resonant to the frequency of the applied voltage. During the negative alternation of the RF generator, electrons will move along the wire, away from point A, toward point B. The electrons are stopped and accumulate at point B, which represents a high voltage point. During the positive alternation of the RF power source, electrons move away from point B and crowd together at point A, which also represents a high voltage point. In the center of the antenna there is, at all times, a maximum movement of electrons, causing a high current or a low voltage point. Therefore, very little voltage will appear at the center of the antenna. On the other hand, there will be a low current at the ends. Figure 15-2 illustrates the voltage and current distribution on a fundamental half wave antenna. This representation of a voltage and current distribution is known as a standing wave pattern. The points of minimum current and minimum voltage are known as current and voltage nodes, respectively. An antenna is said to be resonant when there exist standing waves of voltage and current along its length. Since the waves traveling back and forth in the antenna reinforce each other, a maximum radiation of electro-magnetic waves into space results. When there is no resonance (no standing waves), the waves tend to cancel each other, thus dissipating their energies in the form of heat loss, rather than being radiated into space. Therefore, a resonant antenna connected to an RF generator can dissipate power because most of the energy leaves the antenna in the form of radiation.

ANTENNA IMPEDANCE

Since voltage and current vary along the length of the antenna, a definite impedance value must be associated with each point along the antenna. The impedance varies according to the relative crowding of the electrons as the ends are approached. The impedance existing at any point is simply the voltage at that point, divided by the current at that point. Thus, the lowest impedance occurs where the current is highest (at the center), and the highest impedance occurs where the current is lowest (at the ends).

THE HERTZ ANTENNA

A Hertz antenna is any length of wire far enough from ground so that it will not be influenced by grounded objects. Therefore, its physical length will directly determine the wavelength to which it will tune. A short length antenna will be resonant to a short

wavelength or a high frequency; a long length antenna will be resonant to a long wavelength or low frequency. Therefore, the resonant frequency of a Hertz antenna can be changed by varying its
physical length. This is true because an antenna acts like a resonant circuit. Figure 15-3 illustrates a center fed Hertz half-wave
antenna. Since the center of a half-wave antenna is a high current
point, we say that the antenna is current fed by the transmitter.
The impedance at the center of this Hertz antenna is about 73 ohms.

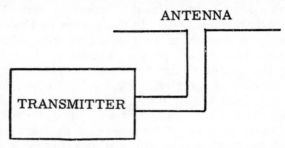

Figure 15-3. Center-fed Hertz antenna.

The impedance rises uniformly towards each end of the antenna,
where it is about 2400 ohms.

PROPAGATION OF RADIO WAVES
     The radio wave that leaves a transmitter takes two general
paths. One path is along the surface of the earth and is called the
GROUND WAVE. The other path is towards the sky and the radiated wave that travels along this path is called the SKY WAVE.
     In traveling along the surface of the earth, the GROUND WAVE
gradually loses its strength until it is completely diminished. On
the other hand, the sky wave can travel for thousands of miles.
     Some distance above the earth, the sky wave strikes a gaseous
mass called the IONOSPHERE. Here, the wave is reflected back to
the earth. (See Fig. 15-4). If a receiver is located between the end
of the ground wave and the point where the sky wave returns to the
earth, it will not pick up the transmitted signal. The area between
the ground wave zone and the point where the sky wave hits the
earth is called the SKIP ZONE. After the wave strikes the earth,
it may again be reflected up to the ionosphere and back to the earth.
In this way, a signal can travel all around the world.
     Frequencies above 50 Mc. generally do not reflect from the
ionosphere. They penetrate the ionosphere and never return to
earth. Thus, for frequencies above 50 Mc. (FM and TV stations),
we depend only upon the ground wave.

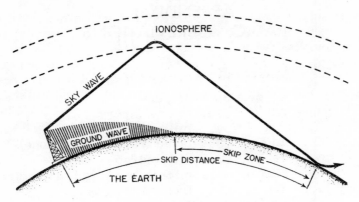

Figure 15-4. Propagation of radio waves.

RECEIVING ANTENNAS

The antenna theory that has been discussed in this chapter applies to receiving antennas as well as to transmitting antennas. In many cases, good reception can be obtained with a makeshift antenna because of strong transmitted signals. However, if the receiving antenna is accurately designed, reception will definitely be better.

In localities where the receivers are located close to the transmitting station, an indoor antenna will operate in a satisfactory manner. Those receivers located far from the transmitting station should have a high outdoor antenna for satisfactory reception.

APPENDIX I
RADIO ABBREVIATIONS

Group	Abbreviation	Meaning
Ampere	a, or amp.	ampere
	μa	microampere
	ma	milliampere
Farad	fd or f	farad (rarely used alone)
	μf	microfarad
	$\mu\mu$f or pf ..	micromicrofarad or picofarad
Frequency	f	frequency
	c* (or).....	cycles
	cps	cycles per second
	kc.	kilocycles per second
	Mc.	Megacycles per second
Henry	h	henry
	mh	millihenry
	μh	microhenry
Impedance	XL	inductive reactance (in ohms)
	XC	capacitive reactance (in ohms)
Ohm	Ω (Omega).	ohm resistance
	MΩ	megohm (one million ohms)
Volt	V	volt
Watt..........	w	watt
	p	power (in watts)
Current.......	AC	alternating current
	DC	direct current
Frequency	AF........	audio frequency
	RF	radio frequency
	IF	intermediate frequency
	TRF.......	tuned radio frequency
Miscellaneous .	CW........	continuous wave
	AM........	amplitude modulation
	FM........	frequency modulation
	EMF (emf)..	electromotive force (in volts)
	MOPA	master oscillator power amplifier
	EST	Eastern Standard Time
	GMT.......	Greenwich Mean Time

*The term "Hertz" has been used in place of cycles in recent years. The abbreviation for Hertz is Hz. We can, therefore, also use the terms kilohertz, megahertz, etc.

APPENDIX 2
COMMON RADIO SYMBOLS

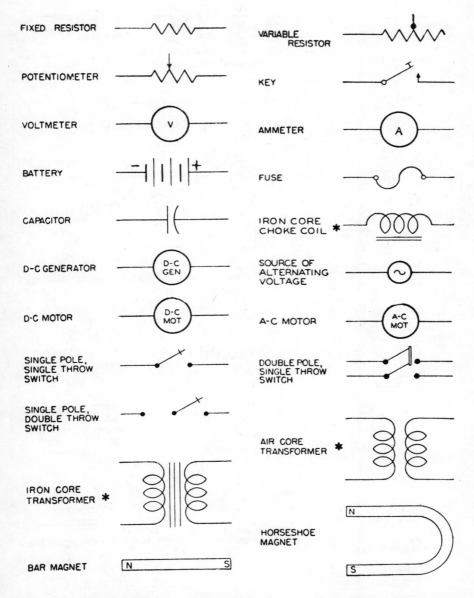

FIXED RESISTOR

VARIABLE RESISTOR

POTENTIOMETER

KEY

VOLTMETER

AMMETER

BATTERY

FUSE

CAPACITOR

IRON CORE CHOKE COIL *

D-C GENERATOR

SOURCE OF ALTERNATING VOLTAGE

D-C MOTOR

A-C MOTOR

SINGLE POLE, SINGLE THROW SWITCH

DOUBLE POLE, SINGLE THROW SWITCH

SINGLE POLE, DOUBLE THROW SWITCH

AIR CORE TRANSFORMER *

IRON CORE TRANSFORMER *

HORSESHOE MAGNET

BAR MAGNET

*Either (OOOO) or _MMM_ may be used to represent coils of wire on chokes or transformers.

APPENDIX 2
COMMON RADIO SYMBOLS

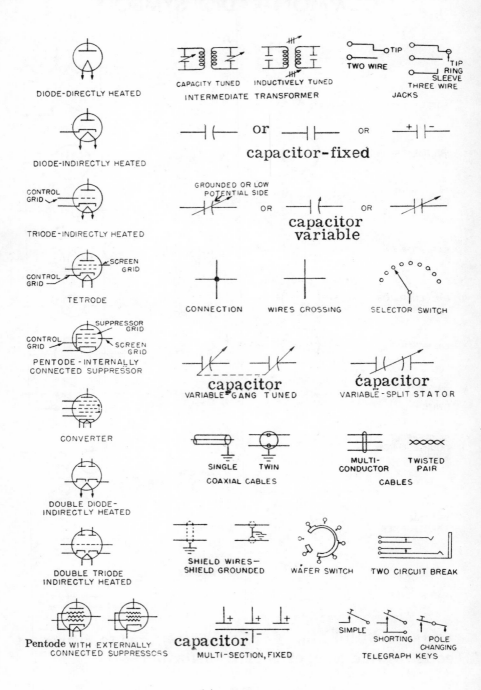

DIODE-DIRECTLY HEATED

DIODE-INDIRECTLY HEATED

TRIODE-INDIRECTLY HEATED

TETRODE

PENTODE - INTERNALLY CONNECTED SUPPRESSOR

CONVERTER

DOUBLE DIODE-INDIRECTLY HEATED

DOUBLE TRIODE INDIRECTLY HEATED

Pentode WITH EXTERNALLY CONNECTED SUPPRESSORS

CAPACITY TUNED   INDUCTIVELY TUNED
INTERMEDIATE TRANSFORMER

TWO WIRE   TIP

TIP
RING
SLEEVE
THREE WIRE
JACKS

or   OR   + −
capacitor-fixed

GROUNDED OR LOW
POTENTIAL SIDE   OR   OR
capacitor
variable

CONNECTION   WIRES CROSSING   SELECTOR SWITCH

capacitor   capacitor
VARIABLE-GANG TUNED   VARIABLE-SPLIT STATOR

SINGLE   TWIN
COAXIAL CABLES

MULTI-CONDUCTOR   TWISTED PAIR
CABLES

SHIELD WIRES—
SHIELD GROUNDED   WAFER SWITCH   TWO CIRCUIT BREAK

capacitor
MULTI-SECTION, FIXED

SIMPLE   SHORTING   POLE CHANGING
TELEGRAPH KEYS

182

APPENDIX 3
RADIO FORMULAS

(Explanations of letters and symbols are on Page 184).

1. Ohm's Law: $\quad I = \dfrac{E}{R} \qquad E = IR \qquad R = \dfrac{E}{I}$

2. Power: $\qquad P = EI \qquad P = I^2 R \qquad P = \dfrac{E^2}{R}$

3. Resistors in Series: $\quad R_T = R_1 + R_2 + R_3 \ldots\ldots\ldots$

4. TWO Resistors in Parallel: $\quad R_T = \dfrac{R_1 \times R_2}{R_1 + R_2}$

5. Resistors in Parallel: $\quad R_T = \dfrac{1}{\dfrac{1}{R_1} + \dfrac{1}{R_2} + \dfrac{1}{R_3} \ldots\ldots\ldots}$

6. Inductors in Series: $\quad L_T = L_1 + L_2 + L_3 \ldots\ldots\ldots$

7. Inductors in Parallel: $\quad L_T = \dfrac{1}{\dfrac{1}{L_1} + \dfrac{1}{L_2} + \dfrac{1}{L_3} \ldots\ldots\ldots}$

8. Inductive Reactance: $\quad X_L = 2\pi fL$

9. Capacitors in Parallel: $\quad C_T = C_1 + C_2 + C_3 \ldots\ldots\ldots$

10. Capacitors in Series: $\quad C_T = \dfrac{1}{\dfrac{1}{C_1} + \dfrac{1}{C_2} + \dfrac{1}{C_3} \ldots\ldots\ldots}$

11. Capacitive Reactance: $\quad X_C = \dfrac{1}{2\pi fC}$

12. Resonant Frequency of a Tuned Circuit: $\quad f_r = \dfrac{1}{2\pi\sqrt{LC}}$

13. Characteristic Impedance of an Air Insulated Parallel Conductor Transmission Line: $\quad Z = 276 \log \dfrac{b}{a}$

APPENDIX 3
RADIO FORMULAS

14. Standing Wave Ratio of
a Transmission Line: $SWR = \dfrac{Imax}{Imin}$ or $\dfrac{Emax}{Emin}$

15. Wavelength of Radio Waves: $\lambda = \dfrac{300,000,000}{f}$

In the Radio Formulas given in this Appendix, please note the following:

I is current in Amperes
E is voltage in volts
R is resistance in ohms
P is power in watts
L is inductance in henries
T stands for total
X_L is inductive reactance in ohms
f is frequency in cycles
C is capacity in farads
X_C is capacitive reactance in ohms
"a" is the radius of the conductor
"b" is the center-to-center distance between conductors
λ is the wavelength in meters
π is called "pi" and is equal to 3.14

INDEX

Triode, 85-92
Triode as an amplifier, 89-92
True power, 56
Tubes (see Vacuum Tubes)
Tuned circuit, 130
Tuned radio frequency
   receiver, 155-160
Tuned radio frequency receiver
   circuit, 159
Turns ratio, 58

U

Undamped wave, 131

V

Vacuum tubes, 62-82, 84-100
Variable inductor, 166
Variable-mu, 157, 169
Variable resistor, 8
Varistor, 126
Velocity microphone, 120-121
Velocity of electromagnetic
   wave, 175
Volt, 9
   kilovolt, 9

Voltage, 9
Voltage, inverse peak, 81
Voltage rating of capacitors, 46
Voltage ratio, 58
Voltage regulation, 80-83
Voltage regulator circuit, 82-83
Voltage regulator tubes, 82
Volt-amperes, 56
Voltmeter, 9, 31
Volume control, 157
Volume control,
   automatic, 168-169

W

Watt, 19
Watt-hour meter, 21
Watt-meter, 20, 56
Wavelength, 175
Wheatstone bridge, 19
Wirewound resistor, 8

X, Y, Z

Zener diode, 83
Zener "knee", 84